Conten

The Author

Nigel Woodrup was born in South Yorkshire in 1961. Farming is in his blood but several generations back. His family moved to East Sussex in 1970, and he became hooked on sheep when he lambed down his first ewe on a friend's farm at the age of 12.

In 1982 he completed a 3 year course at Plumpton Agricultural College and gained a National Diploma in Agriculture. After working for various agricultural businesses he took a job as a motorcycle courier to try to save enough money to start his own farm. Sadly he was knocked off his motorcycle a year later and was paralysed from the chest down, which has confined him to a wheelchair for the rest of his life.

In 1990 he was awarded compensation for his injuries and bought a farm in mid Devon. He and his wife Nicola ran a successful sheep and beef enterprise there for the next 10 years, then moved to a small holding near Crediton with their daughter Molly, where they have a flock of 40 pedigree Wiltshire Horn ewes, 12 chickens, 1 dog and 2 cats. His Creedy flock of Wiltshire Horns won the WHSS National Flock competition 2005.

Introduction

This book is for people who have never kept sheep before but are keen to start a small flock. I hope that those of you who already have a few sheep may find some useful tips as well.

Many people move out to the country and buy a house with some land, then have to decide what to do with their acres. Some people are content to let the neighbouring farmer run his stock on their land; others want more of a challenge and decide that breeding their own sheep and rearing their own lambs would fit the bill.

We have known Nigel since 1997. He farms locally and has kept Wiltshire Horns for a while now. Unfortunately most of the photographs in this book are of our Jacobs, but that is only because they are handy for Michael the photographer, being on the spot!

We would like to thank our neighbour Ian Pincombe for his kindness and co-operation, Mary Baxter for her suggestions, Madonna Maguire BVMS MRCVS for her veterinary input, and Giles Roadnight for all his hard work and computer skills.

We hope you enjoy reading this book, and that it gives you confidence to go out and buy a few sheep of your own. All being well you should have years of pleasure and interest from them as we have done with ours.

Michael Roberts and Sara Roadnight,

Kennerleigh,

Devon.

March 2003

Chapter 1   Buying Sheep

What Breed Should I Buy?

Pure Breeds

There are many breeds of sheep and choosing one will be difficult for the newcomer, but here are some guidelines which should be helpful. Incidentally, it's good to see that nowadays there seems to be a return to the more traditional British breeds after the brief love affair that some people had with Continental breeds.

There are colour charts with photographs of most of the breeds in Britain, but these do not give a very good feel for the animal or its size, so it is best to go to one of the leading agricultural shows to see for yourself. Do remember from the outset that these sheep have been combed, clipped, powdered and oiled for the occasion, but they should give you a good idea of the different types of animal. As a newcomer you may well be drawn to the visually exciting looking breeds with prick ears, large horns, woolly faces, spotted coats and curly or straight fleeces, but some of these can be very challenging to keep!

It's a good idea to do some reading about the different breeds before you start out, as well as establishing which are local to your area or region. This is where the Rare Breeds Survival Trust comes in useful, as they have lists of breeds that need your support, and can put you in touch with breeders. Also, there is a very useful book available called British Sheep which describes all the breeds of sheep in the U.K. It is published by the N.S.A. (see Useful Names and Addresses at the back of this book)

It is always worth checking prices as certain breeds attract a following and this can raise prices artificially high. The general advice is to go for an all purpose (fleece and meat) medium sized breed, not too big as large sheep are very tough on your back when you are handling them, and not too small as primitive breeds, which are often very small, can be rather wild and difficult to contain. Also, some of the broad backed sheep are prone to getting 'cast', that is stuck on their backs.

There are several ways for the beginner to approach sheep keeping. It's essential that you have good advice, so you need to befriend a local person who keeps sheep, but try to avoid anyone who kept them 'a few years ago', as they are probably not familiar with the ins and outs of today's paperwork, or the latest drugs for dealing with worms etc. It's possible that you could become involved in an extended breeding programme for this person's flock which could have many advantages, but you do need someone to help you buy your sheep and ensure that you are not being 'done'. You will also rely on this person to help with the management of your sheep to begin with, and be there in case of emergencies or if you are away on holiday. A tall order certainly, but if you can find such a paragon and show them proper appreciation they should help you whenever they can!

Where to buy:

Try to avoid general markets as you don't know what problems you may be buying. It is best to approach breeders direct or buy at specialist shows and sales which are run by the breed societies or the Rare Breeds Survival Trust. Always take your sheep advisor with you and be prepared to walk away from stock that does not come up to the required standard. You have to remember that the seller is not letting his best animals go unless he is retiring, so the sheep he is selling will not be quite up to the mark. Having said that, you are buying into that breeding line, and I know from experience that although certain ewes may not look terrific, they can produce first class lambs.

Each breeder will of course tell you the advantages of their own particular breed; you will get all the spiel about easy lambing and fast maturing lambs, good feet, no shearing, docile etc., most of which may be true, but don't be too swayed by this as he / she is only doing a good sales job. It is also advisable to visit the breeder on their farm to get a better impression of their animals and how they are kept. Breeders normally sell their surplus stock any time between July and October depending on when they lamb their ewes. It is best to buy ewe lambs. Buying adult ewes can be buying trouble, but not always.

If you just want some sheep as 'lawn mowers', there are several options to choose from. Maybe you have a limited amount of land, you don't want to have livestock on it in the winter because it floods or gets poached quickly, and you don't want to have to deal with lambing or winter feeding.

- Option 1: Let your field out to the local farmer and run his sheep or rams on it during the grass growing months of the summer.

- Option 2: Buy some ewe store lambs in July or August to run on your land until October. These are lambs that have been weaned from their mothers but require more time to mature, either for the freezer or for breeding. An advantage is that they will not need shearing. You should be able to buy some from your local market or farmer, but you will need advice so that at the end of October you have a saleable product.

- Option 3: Have a non-breeding flock. This is a group of ewes or castrated males (wethers) who are not put to the ram but are kept solely for grazing grass, and perhaps also for their wool. They are kept all the year round, become very tame and can have a lifespan of 20 years or more.

- Option 4: Buy some 'couples' i.e. ewes with lamb(s) at foot then sell the offspring as fat lambs and either keep the ewes or sell them in the Autumn.

Buying In A Ram Or Ewes

When you go to buy a ram or some ewes there are some points you should look out for. A good animal should stand proud with its head held high and its ears pricked. It should have clear eyes that watch your every move and a long straight back with a good strong leg at each corner. Every breed will call for different specifications, weight, colour of horns, shoulder height, facial markings etc, so you will need to look long and hard at any animal you are going to buy. If you are buying a ram you will need to check that his testicles are long and even and firm to the touch.

Left: Look for good straight legs
Right: Avoid bow legs

Apart from these visual characteristics, the animal must be clean at both ends: no runny eyes or noses, (check the eyelids for split lids) and at the other end, any clipping round the tail which might mean runny faeces, implying internal problems. Listen to the breathing. Make sure that it is not laboured or wheezy and that there is no persistent cough which could be lungworm or pneumonia. Check for missing wool, either clipped or rubbed off. It could mean the animal has been fly struck or worse, could have Scab, (see Diseases).

Check the feet. Look out for lameness and smell any bad feet. When you get

Left: Poor Foot
Right: Correct foot

these sheep back home, trim all their feet and if possible, stand them in a foot bath of Zinc Sulphate, (see Diseases). Worm them with Ivomectin and Levamisole and keep them indoors for 48 hours before you release them into their field.

Check their mouths. Make sure that the gum on top meets the teeth below neatly; you are looking for under or over-shot bottom jaws. Check the teeth. These will give an indication of age.

Scoring

Feel across the back of the sheep behind the last rib to check the condition of the animal. This is called scoring and it rates from 0 to 5: 0 is skin and bone and 5 is a very fat animal. The back bone should feel like a round log, not a spiny branch. All sheep mature at varying rates so don't be surprised to find different scores in a single pen of lambs. The best way to check a lamb's weight is to weigh it.

Ewes' udders must be checked; they must have two teats and be soft and spongy to the touch.

If you decide to buy all wethers, make sure they have been properly castrated and that there are no rigs among them. A rig is a ram that has not been castrated properly, see section on Castration.

Finally, when buying for the first time, take someone with you who knows the breed you are buying so that you don't end up with a poor starter flock. It is far better to pay a little more and get some good animals than go for bargain ones which could cause trouble. Don't buy too many to begin with as they will soon multiply, and half the pleasure of keeping sheep is breeding your own. It is best to buy ewe lambs and ram lambs as they adjust better to your conditions.

Most of these points still apply if you are just buying in store lambs for the freezer to run on to autumn or winter. Obviously the breeding aspect is not important, but do buy lambs which will give you a good carcass at the end of the day.

In certain parts of the country, having done a deal on the price of the animals you have bought, it is a tradition to give the vendor "Luck Money". This is normally £10 depending on the size of the purchase, and it is a good will gesture should anything go wrong with your purchase.

Horned Or Polled Sheep

Most commercial flocks are polled, that is they breed naturally without horns. One reason for this is that most shearers today don't like to handle horned sheep because the horns get in the way of their work and do tend to stick into the shearer, sometimes in vulnerable places!

Although horns can be useful as handles when you are dealing with your sheep, you must treat them with caution as they can sometimes come off in your hand, leaving a bloody mess. Rams' horns are usually fairly sturdy. Horned sheep can become snagged in wire fencing and electric netting. We once had a ewe who constantly pushed her head through the wire and got stuck, very often when everyone had just gone to bed, (or that's how it seemed). A plaintive bleating would start up and we would know exactly who it was. I made her a pair of wooden 'antlers', just a straight piece of wood 1.5" x 1" attached round the base of her horns with a chin strap and that stopped the problem.

Some breeds have problems with horns, particularly those of the rams, which can grow into the sides of their faces. You will have to seek advice on this from a vet or someone else with experience of sheep

Rams – Should I Keep One?

There are two important questions to think about before deciding to keep a ram: first, how do I get my ewes served or tupped, and second, is there enough space to keep one?

The ram is responsible for 50% of the genetic make up of your lambs, so he does play an important part in your flock. If you are bringing in or hiring a ram, there is always the possibility of bringing in something else as well, disease perhaps, or parasites.

You shouldn't have a problem hiring or borrowing a ram, but can you hire him when you want him? This is not always easy to organise, and you can end up lambing later than intended. Before you put him in with your ewes, check and wash his feet and make sure that he is clean behind.

The ram needs to be separated from the ewes for 7 or 8 months of the year, so you will need a small well fenced paddock to put him in during that time, preferably out of sight of the ewes. He will be joined by the ram lambs, castrated or not, until they go for breeding or to the abattoir. (In commercial flocks the rams are only put in with the ewes during the tupping period.) It is important also, not to keep the ram isolated for too long as he may become too friendly. This friendliness can turn to aggression during the tupping season, which could be dangerous if you are in the field with them. On the other hand he can become just plain aggressive from boredom. Keep an eye open for him starting to walk backwards a few paces, it's a sure sign you're in for a charge! Some people keep a wether, (a castrated male sheep) as a companion for the ram, but this may not always be practical for the small flock owner. A teaser is a vasectomised ram which is put in with the ewes to bring them into oestrus so they will be ready for tupping.

If you keep more than one ram, be warned that they will fight if they can see or smell ewes coming into season. They have even been known to kill each other by neck dislocation from head butting. So rams have to be introduced to each other out of the tupping season and well away from the ewes. Shearing is sometimes a problem as they don't recognize each other after their fleeces are taken off, and fighting can break out; so put them into a small holding pen quite tightly to allow their smells to rub off on each other. There are ram masks available. These are pieces of leather which are strapped over the rams' faces preventing them from seeing in front. They work well but can become loose or slip off. Don't think that a stout fence will keep two rams apart either, as they will demolish it in no time.

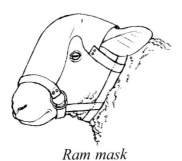

Ram mask

Some people like to record when their ewes were mated, and this is possible if you put a raddle on your ram. A raddle is a harness that fits on the ram's body with a colour marking block on his chest. The ewe's rump will be marked when she is served. You can use different colours for different rams or periods. This system is not really necessary for the small flock owner as normally your ewes will all be mated within 10 to 21 days. There was a story told about a walker who accosted a farmer and asked why his sheep had got graffiti on them, so now you know the answer!

Chapter 2   Routine

Annual Routine

Sheep are a commitment involving several busy periods during the year, but these can be easily planned in advance. Lambing, shearing, foot trimming and taking lambs to the abattoir are the main events in the sheep calendar, interspersed with long periods when nothing happens to them except a daily check by you walking round them while they munch your grass. Regular observation is at the heart of stockmanship, so you will be on the lookout for any animals limping or caught in the hedge, or anything unusual and different from normal.

Here is a simple breakdown of monthly sheep activities throughout the year:

- **January:** routine daily check, supplementary daily feed of hay and concentrates, last foot trimming before lambing. Take out the ram.

- **February:** routine daily check, supplementary daily feed of hay and concentrates.

- **March:** routine daily check, supplementary daily feed of hay and concentrates.

- **April**: lambing, allow 4 weeks. Routine daily check, supplementary daily feed of hay and concentrates. Foot trimming and worming of ewes after lambing.

- **May:** routine daily check. Plenty of fresh grass now so end supplementary daily feed

- **June**: routine twice daily check for Fly Strike (see page 76), first week shearing, Vetrazine (anti Fly Strike), hay making June / July.

- **July:** routine twice daily check for Fly Strike, foot trimming.

- **August:** routine twice daily check for Fly Strike, Vetrazine (anti Fly Strike), take out all ram lambs, if entire.

- **September:** routine twice daily check for Fly Strike.

- **October:** routine daily check, foot trimming.

- **November:** routine daily check, put ram in for breeding, take lambs to abattoir, supplementary daily feed of hay and concentrates.

- **December:** routine daily check, supplementary daily feed of hay and concentrates.

Sheep must be visited daily and during the Fly Strike period, June to September, twice a day. The guide above is just an approximate one and may well vary from one end of the country to the other.

The specific jobs mentioned will take you less time as you gain experience and build up your equipment; here is a rough breakdown of the time involved if you have about 10 ewes:

- Supplementary feeding of hay and concentrates 10 – 20 minutes per day

- Foot trimming 1 – 1 hour 30 minutes

- Lambing. The ewes must be checked every few hours, day and night until lambing is over, approximately 4 weeks

- Vetrazine 30 minutes

- Shearing 1 - 2 hours. Professionals take from 2 to 5 minutes to shear an animal.

A small hay shed

Three different ways to mark sheep

Broken horn from careless handling

Hampshire Down (H. Derryman, Honiton)

Dorset Down

Wiltshire Horn Ram (N. Woodrup, Crediton)

Greyfaced Dartmoor (V. Pratt, Temple Combe)

Clun Forest

Poll Dorset (N. Jesse, Salisbury)

A broken coat

A full coat

Showing where to score on a sheep's back

- Lambs for slaughter 2 hours preparation

- 2 – 3 hours for delivery

These times are only approximate and will obviously vary according to the time of year, the weather and the number of sheep involved. It's important to realize that there will always be the odd day when something goes wrong, an accident for instance or Fly Strike, and you will have to be able to act immediately or be able to call on someone else to do so.

Chapter 3 Equipment

Fencing

This is an important topic in its own right. Before you go buying sheep or putting them into a rented field, it is vital to ensure that there is a good perimeter fence, hedge or wall. First of all, you don't want your sheep wandering off over your neighbour's land, crops or garden; secondly, if your sheep get out onto the road you are liable for prosecution, and thirdly, you don't want your neighbour's sheep or ram coming onto your land. So a secure perimeter fence is essential.

It is very important when fencing not to leave behind any metal staples or small bits of wire on the grass as sheep have a nasty habit of eating these, resulting in serious problems such as traumatic reticulitis; so always pick up any bits and pieces that may have been dropped before putting your stock in the field.

If you don't know much about fencing or even if you think you know a little, it is wise to go on a fencing course, as you can save yourself time and money and in the end have a fence that lasts. It could also be useful during the quieter times of year as you could do some contract work for local farmers. If you haven't the time to do your own fencing, bring in a fencing contractor to do the job properly.

If you have enough land try to make separate fields so you can rotate your sheep and help to keep the worm burden from building up, (more on this later). It may also involve refencing your property and changing gateways, and if you are able to, fencing off wet or boggy areas and putting in shelter belts etc. Don't forget that you will be moving your sheep from one area to another and bear this in mind when organising your gateways. A large field can be fenced across, but it might be better to use electric fencing which is ideal for fencing off areas to put your sheep in but not as a permanent method of fencing. There are several reasons for this. First, the wire netting can short when the grass gets longer; the sheep will realize this and push over the fence if they are hungry. Then if the fencing unit is powered by a battery, this can run down and of course render the fence useless. Thirdly, fence units have a habit of getting pinched, so always put them out of view of the general public or away from the road. Finally, a word of warning: electric netting fences will kill lambs of horned breeds. They get their heads stuck in the netting and die.

When refencing your property, you must consider tractor access for mowing, rolling, topping and hedge cutting. The rollers are the widest pieces of equipment you will be taking through your gateways. Straight lines are easy to work with, narrow necks of land are not. You can always use irregular corners of ground for your ram when he is not running with the flock.

Water

This is required all the time. Although sheep do not appear to drink much as they take in water from wet grass, it is surprising the amount they do consume, particularly when they have just lambed, are lactating or eating hay, or when the weather is hot. A plastic tub or tank works well for the small flock owner. Keep it topped up and give it a good clean out periodically during the summer and autumn months. It can be moved round with the sheep. Buckets of water are fine in lambing pens but tend to get knocked over in a field. Also, sheep with horns have difficulty getting their heads into buckets.

If you can join up with mains water, use some blue plastic pipe and plastic fittings. These are easy to assemble, and in cold weather the ice in the pipes will push the fittings off rather than bursting the pipes.

Metal Hurdles, Troughs, Hay Racks

These are all available from your local agricultural dealer, or if you have some carpentry skills you could get a copy of the book in the Gold Cockerel Series called 'The Smallholder's DIY'. Alternatively, these items frequently go for sale at farm auctions. The prices are normally quite low and you could find some bargains.

Equipment

Here is a list of what you will need: a good pair of foot trimming clippers, foot spray, aerosol marker, rub on marker, several sizes of syringe and needles. The most frequently used item in this list is the foot trimming clippers, and everything is available from your local agricultural dealer. You will also need an aerosol can of Terramycin for foot work and cuts, but you will have to get this from your local vet.

Housing

Do I need to bring my sheep in for the winter? The answer is normally no. However, if you have the maximum stock for your land, or it floods and lies wet in the winter, or you are planning to lamb early, then the answer must be yes.

There are several points that should be thought through before you decide to construct a sheep house or barn:

A. You may need to get Planning Permission.

B. The siting of your building is all important. You must consider how it will affect your neighbours, how good is the access from the public road, and what direction the prevailing winds come from.

C. Where is the nearest supply of mains or private water?

D. The same for

. This is important not only for feeding and checking your animals at either end of the day, but also for shearing. Where is the nearest supply?

E.   The height of the building. You must leave enough height to allow vehicular access into the building with a tractor or Bobcat, when you are cleaning out after lambing, for example.

If this all sounds too expensive and difficult to organize, there is always the possibility of putting up a polytunnel. These are used quite often for lambing, and have the advantage of being easy to move, so that bacteria have no chance to build up.

The important thing to remember when planning a building for sheep is to keep the design as flexible as possible. Don't forget to make enough room to store your hay and straw as well.

The building must be light and airy without being draughty; use Yorkshire boarding and Netlon curtains to cut down the wind without reducing the airflow. Ventilation is most important: sheep do not need to be kept warm, they have plenty of their own insulation. In fact some commercial sheep farmers shear their ewes before housing them so that they won't get too warm indoors, and also because they take up less space without their fleeces on. (It has been found that indoor lambs seem to do better if their mothers have been shorn. It may be that they find their mothers' teats more easily without the long wool in the way.) So a good flow of air through the shed is essential to prevent a close or muggy atmosphere from building up, particularly on foggy or mild winter days.

Rain and snow are a problem as they will wet the bedding where they blow in, so plan an access corridor on the 'wet' side of the building.

The 'furniture', that is the hurdles and troughs, etc. must all be moveable so they can be taken out for cleaning after lambing and allow the tractor in to muck out the building.

One end of the barn must be dedicated to the storage of hay and straw; it is best to have them both under the same roof, as carrying bales across a muddy yard can make feeding your livestock a chore, and in these circumstances things can get missed or forgotten and then the stock suffers.

Remember that when sheep are indoors their feet grow rapidly, so their litter must be as dry as possible and their feet must be trimmed regularly.

Pen sizes vary but are normally about 6' x 4', (1.83 metres x 1.22 metres) per ewe and lambs. You may need to adjust this according to the breed of sheep and the number of lambs. Each pen will need a hay rack which straddles the hurdle and is shared with the next door pen, a water bucket, (there are bucket brackets available which clip onto the hurdle) and a feed container for or rolled oats etc. The container can be a purpose made hook-on trough, or a washing up bowl will do.

Normally the ewe and lamb(s) will only be indoors for a few days, so as soon as a pen becomes empty it can be cleaned out and thoroughly disinfected. This is important because the old straw in the pen will still contain pieces of afterbirth etc, which will generate harmful and smelly bacteria.

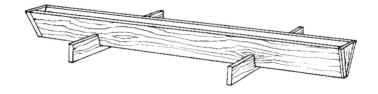

Chapter 4   Grass and Hay

Looking After Your Grass

When you buy your property, check to see if the land has been used for sheep in the past. If it has, you should rest the ground for a year. This will help clear it of parasites and bacteria, and will ensure that the new clean sheep which you introduce, will not be infected by any bugs.

While your fields are resting you will have to deal with grass which of course keeps on growing. There are two ways of doing this: if you have time you can mow it regularly and the clippings will mulch the grass and help to feed it, or you might be lucky enough to find a local farmer who needs ground for silage or haymaking, but you will still have to keep it mown in late summer and autumn.

Mowing is done with a tractor-mounted grass topper or mower. One of the best and strongest on the market is the Votex mower from Hereford; (Michael Roberts tells me he has had one for over 20 years!) One of the beauties of this machine is that you can mow backwards as well as forwards which is very useful for getting into the corners of fields.

While resting your ground you have a good opportunity to deal with any weeds that are there. The main ones to look out for are thistles, docks, nettles and ragwort. I am not a chemical user, (although I will use them if I have to) so I normally dig out thistles, docks and ragwort with a small fork or spade, and use a wheelbarrow to cart them away. If there are masses, just do 20 minutes a day and clear a small patch at a time. Dry the plants and burn them. If you mow or strim nettles or creeping thistles regularly, starting in early Spring, you will find that they gradually give up and disappear after 2 or 3 years.

If you want to increase your grass yield, give it a feed of calcified seaweed. This comes in heavy plastic bags (50 kilos) and should be applied about 4 bags to the acre. It is a slow release calcium and looks like ground coral or seashells, and really improves the grass. It can be spread with an ordinary fertilizer spreader mounted on the back of a tractor or trailed behind a quad bike. You will have to adjust the spinning mechanism for this product. Don't use nitrogen on your field: although it is a quick release fertilizer, it burns all the herbs and wild flowers.

While your fields are resting you also have an opportunity to sort out the boundaries: make sure the fencing is secure, and cut back and clear out any brambles in the hedges. These can be a real nuisance as they will hold a sheep by its fleece. Nine times out of ten when you go to release the animal, armed with leather gloves and secateurs, it will pull itself free as you approach, but it could be subject to predation if left alone. Fence off woodland and spinneys and if you have any wet areas, you can divide them off for conservation.

If you are taking over existing grass fields, they may well need a good going over with a chain harrow to pull out all the old dead grass and break up any lumps of manure. This is normally done in the Spring.

It is better to have too few sheep than too many, but if you find that your grass is growing too fast for them, it will need topping with a tractor mower. Long wet grass is not good for sheep as it tends to make them scour and their faeces become very runny, a sign that their insides can't cope with the lushness of the grass. This in turn makes the sheep's back and tail very mucky and attracts flies, and then there is the possibility of Fly Strike and maggots.

Grazing on Rented Ground

The small flock owner is normally a person of few acres. He or she often rents fields from neighbouring people who have bought a place in the country with a paddock or surrounding land to protect them against development, and they are usually delighted to have their paddocks grazed.

There are certain criteria here that the small flock owner should be aware of. The fencing must be strong and secure. This may have to be organized as a jointly funded project, the landlord providing the materials and you providing the labour, perhaps. The field may need topping, (mowing) once or twice a year so that it keeps tidy and free of weeds. Your sheep must all be in good condition with no 'limpers'. Hedge trimming can be sorted out with the landlord and the local agricultural contractor. Do be careful of any trees, shrubs or hedging that your landlord has planted in or on the edge of the field as, if your sheep find anything new and tasty, they are quite capable of browsing up to six feet high, and could do a lot of damage, depending on the breed.

These parcels of land are often some distance from each other and you will have to transport your sheep in a trailer from place to place; so you will need a set of metal hurdles to make a pen from which to load them up. Once they get the hang of going up a ramp into a trailer, they will be less inclined to be awkward in future. Don't forget to keep a record of all your movements (see Records page 61), useful for your own future reference as well as for the bureaucrats.

Money does not normally change hands in this sort of situation, but it does rather depend on the size of ground you are borrowing. It's a good idea to offer your landlord some lamb for his freezer, and this could vary from half a lamb to several whole ones.

If there is a problem with your sheep, look sharp and get in there as soon as possible to sort it out. People like your landlord who have bought properties such as this, are often professionals and as such expect good service. If the word gets round that you are efficient and do your job well, you will be surprised by the amount of grazing that you are offered!

Hay Making

Set aside the field or area you require to make hay on. There are several operations involved if you want to get the maximum yield from your acres, and the first is an application of calcified seaweed put on with a fertilizer spreader. Next, chain harrow and roll the field with a flat heavy roller. This is particularly necessary if you have stony or flinty ground and helps to protect the blades of the grass mower when the hay is cut. The field needs to be shut up, that is no access for animals, in early May.

Hay can be made in June, July or even August, but the earlier you cut it the better, before the grass has had a chance to become stalky and unpalatable. So try to make it in June or early July, weather permitting. There are many different ways to make hay and they vary from one end of the country to the other according to the geography, the climate and the local conditions. However this is how we make hay in Devon.

Talk to your friendly local farmer and ask if he can cut your hay for you. Try to pick a settled 4 or 5 days and ask him to mow it after lunch when the sugar levels in the grass are high. Mowing doesn't take much time with these new drum mowers, and a 6 acre field is soon cut in about an hour.

I usually borrow a hay turner or hay 'bob' so that I can deal with my hay independently of the farmer. You will also need to borrow a tractor if you haven't got one.

When the grass has been cut leave it where it is to wilt for the first day or two. The next morning take your hay turner into the field and start to pile up or 'row' the cut grass in lines. Begin at the outside and try to draw the hay away from under trees or hedges so that the sun can get to it. Allow the ground between the rows to heat up and dry out, and then in the afternoon change the setting on the hay turner so that it will scatter and spread the rowed grass out to dry. Continue with this rowing and spreading for 3 to 5 days. The idea is that the grass should 'cook' from underneath as well as on top. If you have some thick areas of grass, take a fork and redistribute it onto the thinner areas. This happens sometimes at the ends of the rows.

When the hay is ready it should be light, airy and sweet smelling with no green patches left anywhere. Hay will soon go mouldy if the grass is baled while still damp or green. Your next task is to row it all up for the baler. It is best to get your baling done in the afternoon before the evening dew. You will be able to tell if the hay is good by the weight of the bales. The ones from the outside of the field are always heavier than those from the middle which is why it is important to row the grass in from the edges, even if it tends to make the outside rows rather large to begin with. Naturally you can't always rely on the weather, but after a shower of rain always row the crop and allow the ground to dry before spreading the grass again. Keeping the grass rowed during rainy weather helps the wind to dry it, and stops the new grass from growing through the cut hay.

Once your hay is baled, load it onto trailers and remove it from the field for storage. A dry bale of hay is like a sponge and needs to be kept out of the wet.

Storing Hay

Get your barn or shed ready before you start hay making. The storage is almost as important as the making of the hay, because if it is badly stored it not only becomes mouldy and rotten without proper ventilation, but the bales can get misshapen and will be difficult to handle. (This can be caused by shrinkage as the bales dry out, or by the hay being baled too loosely in the first place, but you will have to rely on the farmer not to let that happen.) If the barn or shed is exposed to the weather, the sides should have a breathable membrane or Yorkshire boarding put in place to stop the outside bales from getting wet. The membrane must be breathable as hay needs good ventilation, but if it gets damp at all, it will heat up and there could be a risk of fire. Even a nail hole in the roof where water can drip through, will cause a rotten bale or two.

Put down a damp course membrane plastic sheet first, even if there is a concrete floor, and then put slatted wooden pallets on top. Tuck the side curtains under the pallets to stop the wind. The reason for the plastic sheet on the floor is that in the autumn and winter the concrete sweats, the soil gives off moisture, and the bottom bales will suck up the damp and be ruined. The pallets not only raise the bales from the floor but also allow the air to circulate. In the old days a layer of straw was used for this purpose but that was when straw was cheap. It was also put down to encourage rats to forage in it for food rather than spoil the hay.

Always start stacking your bales from the outside and work inwards to ensure vertical sides. The first layer of bales is laid edgeways and not flat. There are two reasons for this: the bales keep their shape better and therefore provide a stable platform, and secondly the bale strings are not so accessible for rats to bite through which could cause the stack to be unstable. Another point is that baler twine used to be made of hessian and would rot if it came in contact with the ground. If the hay is a bit damp coming in from the field, it is important to stack the bales with air corridors to allow them to dry and breathe. After the first layer they should be laid down flat, with the bales in each layer lying at right angles to those in the layer below. This helps to make the stack stable, safe and neat. It is always nice to open up the first bales when you start to feed your hay, and smell summer again, even though the weather may be vile outside!

Well made hay will last for 2 years for sheep, and longer for cows and horses. It does tend to lose its palatability for sheep after two years.

Chapter 5   Shearing

During May and June, depending on the weather, your flocks' wool will start to rise. This is when the fleece appears to be coming away from the skin, normally seen around the neck, and this natural process helps lift the wool when shearing.

Shearers like to be in and out as quickly as possible so it is important to be ready for them. There are quite a few things that need to be organized before your shearer turns up on the day.

First of all, he cannot shear wet sheep so keep them in overnight or for part of a day. This is also an advantage because sheep are best shorn with empty stomachs, so make sure that they have no food for about 12 hours beforehand, but keep water available.

Work out where the shearing is going to take place, ideally under cover in a barn or under a tree.

You will need a supply of electricity and a beam to hang the electric motor from.

Work out a handling system for your sheep so that they are easily accessible and have somewhere to go after they have been dealt with. Try to keep the lambs separate; they are not usually shorn.

Clean up the back ends of your sheep if they are dirty, so that the fleeces are kept clean. Some shearers object to working with dirty sheep.

The shearer needs a wooden floor or a piece of 8' x 4' (2.44 x 1.22 metres), plyboard to work on. He will not shear on a concrete or stone floor for fear of breaking the teeth on the clipper combs.

You will need a clean area about 10' x 6', (3.05 x 1.83 metres) nearby where the fleeces can be sorted and rolled up.

Keep a plastic sack handy for bits of dirty wool and a broom to sweep up now and then. Remember, any hay, grass or straw in the fleece downgrades it.

Make sure that the equipment the shearer brings with him has been disinfected. My sheep once picked up a very contagious disease (the sheep version of New Forest Disease which affects the eyes of cattle) from a dirty carpet a shearer used to shear them on.

Shearing can be thirsty work on a hot day, so mugs of tea or cold drinks are a must.

It is often convenient to trim your sheeps' feet while they are still penned up after being shorn. Do not Vetrazine them for another week or so to give the wool time to grow back a bit as it will then absorb the medication more thoroughly.

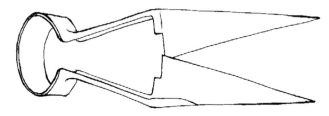

Fleeces

There are two markets for your fleeces. First there are local spinners and weavers. This market is very small and specialized however, with many of these people keeping their own sheep to supply their needs; but it is always worth getting in touch with these organizations.

The other market for fleeces is the Wool Marketing Board, an organization which relies on world wool prices and selling to the clothing and carpet trade. They don't like coloured wool. I learnt this when I heard of someone who took them 18 Jacob fleeces a few years ago and received a cheque totaling 28 pence for them in return!!.....

The problem with shearing at the moment, (2002) is that what you get per fleece, in the case of some breeds, just about covers the cost of the shearer.

This is possibly why some people go for sheep like Wiltshire Horns that do not require shearing. On the other hand it would be sensible to look at breeds with a higher value on their wool.

Rolling a fleece

Fleeces are always rolled up inside out (see pictures). Roll tightly from the tail end of the fleece, and before you reach the other end, twist the remaining wool into a 'rope', wrap it round the fleece and then tuck it inside to secure it. You will then have a compact roll with the inside wool on the outside so that the quality can be easily assessed for grading. They are then sent to the Wool Marketing Board in large canvas bags called sheets. These bags will hold about 15 fleeces, depending on the size and type of sheep. Once filled the bags need to be sewn up and labelled. It important to obtain a registration number from the Wool Marketing Board, who also supply the sheets.

Dipping

If you are in the U.K. you will need a license to buy dipping chemicals and a license to dip your sheep, so you will need to refer to DEFRA for up to date details on the subject. Most smallholders use 'pour-ons' to treat lice, fleas, fly strike, scab, etc. but dipping is actually a more efficient method of dealing with these problems.

Which dip to use? There is really no choice. The non-organic is cheaper but contains harmful OPs, (organo-phosphates) which should have been banned years ago but still continue to be marketed. Organic dips like Crowvect are kinder but contain pyrethrum which is lethal to pond and stream life, so the location of your dipping site is all important.

Most people try to incorporate the dipping area with the general sheep handling area, but this may not always be feasible if there are drains, water courses or ditches nearby. The dipping site should always be located well away from water courses of any kind.

There are several types of dipping containers or baths available. The best for the small flock owner is the 'swim around' type rather than the 'trench' type; the latter requires more water and thus more chemicals, and is often too narrow for horned breeds. It is really only suitable for the larger flock owner who needs to run several hundreds of sheep through in a day.

The 'swim around' type is a precast concrete / fiberglass container with narrow steps at the end where the sheep climb out. It holds from 100 to 200 gallons of water. The sheep are pushed in bottom first and swirled round for about a minute. Their heads are pushed under a couple of times before they are allowed out.

When installing the dipping bath, allow for about 4 feet of standing area round the sides with a larger area on the exit side where the sheep can stand and shake themselves. All these surrounding areas must be made of smooth concrete and slope gently back towards the container. There should be 4 foot walls round three sides of the dipping area to contain any splashes. It is important to incorporate an overflow pipe near the top of the bath to drain off excess rain water in the winter. This pipe should of course be closed during dipping.

Whichever kind of dip you decide on, you need to be thoroughly protected when using it. This involves a hat, goggles or wrap-round glasses, a mouth / nose mask, waterproof gloves, coat and trousers and of course rubber boots, all rather hot when dealing with sheep on a warm day! You will also need a dipping iron or fork for handling the sheep in the bath. You can see now why it is important to plan all the details of your dipping area very carefully so as to avoid unnecessary exertion in all your rubber gear!

Once the sheep are enclosed you do need to have someone 'feeding' them through to the bath. When they get out they will stand for a while in the draining off area shaking the dip out of their ears and coats. From time to time, depending on the number of sheep you put through, you may need to top up the container with water and chemical to keep it to the required strength.

Below is a plan which we have found to work well

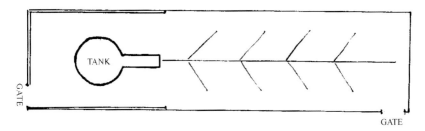

Suggested plan for dipping layout

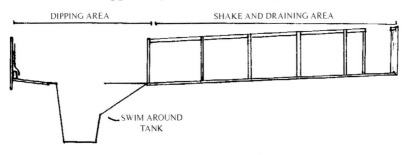

Side view of diagram above

When all the sheep have been dipped, hose down everything back into the bath. (Because I chose to put my dipping area in a small wood, I was able to bale out the dip solution from the container and pour it round the trees. This worked well, the chemical didn't kill the grass or the trees, and seemed to have no ill effects on the area, quite the reverse.)

At the bottom of the bath you will find a sludge of soil, faeces and wool which can be scooped out with a dustpan. When everything is clean cover the bath with sheets of corrugated iron and put several concrete blocks on top to hold them in place. This stops leaves and debris falling in and prevents birds from drowning, and meanwhile the rain fills up the container free of charge ready for next time!

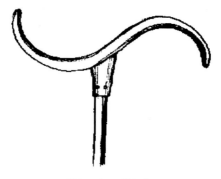

Dipping Stick

Chapter 6 Sales

Sales from Sheep

These fall into six categories: breeding sheep, rams, meat, wool, skins and horns.

Breeding Sheep

Prices fluctuate all the time and a lot depends on the breed; some are more sought after than others and this will determine the price. Blood lines and Scrapie rating tests will also have a good deal to do with it, so surplus pedigree ewe lambs or adult ewes can be sold for as little as £35.00 each or as much as £200.00 each. More may be paid at auctions. In 2005 a Wiltshire Horn shearling ewe sold for 450 guineas.

Rams

Again, a lot depends on the breed, the blood line and the Scrapie rating. Rams can go for £60.00 to £500.00 each. In September 2005 a Wiltshire Horn ram sold for 1,000 guineas. I noticed in the newspaper the other day, that a Swaledale ram from a part of Cumbria ravaged by Foot and Mouth in 2001, fetched £101,000.00 at auction, but that was very unusual!

Meat

The only way for the small flock owner to sell his meat is to market it direct to the public. You get your lambs killed and jointed at the abattoir but if you know how to butcher meat, you can ask for the whole carcass back and do it yourself, thus making a saving. Marketing meat can be done in various ways, the cheaper the better, as slaughtering fees at the moment are about £18.00 per animal. So a whole lamb can be sold for £55.00 to £75.00 including the cost of labels, packing and advertising, depending where you are in the country. You could also go down the organic route but this would require the time for you to get organic status and to be registered as such. It is important to remember that it is illegal to send to the abattoir any animal that is under medication or still within the withdrawal period of any medication.

Presentation of your meat is all important. Trim off any odd bits and remove any chips of bone. Most of your meat will go straight into the freezer so weigh each joint and pack it in the correct size freezer bag, noting the contents and the weight in kilos and pounds. Chops and half joints can be packed on polystyrene trays. Put jointed whole and half lambs in the freezer in separate bags, and when they are required by the customer, they can be transferred into cardboard boxes. There are several types of packing fillers on the market to help keep the contents frozen, but good presentation is a must. It does help to put in a covering letter about your meat and the animals on the farm, together with any cooking tips you may have. Of course your name, address and telephone number must be there as well.

Marketing small quantities of meat is not difficult as most people will be happy to buy half a lamb for £25.00 to £35.00, particularly when you think that you can pay £12 to £15 for a single joint in a supermarket! A half lamb consists of two joints, leg and shoulder, a breast of lamb and about a dozen chops.

To advertise your meat, make up some small posters or cards and distribute them round schools, factories, offices and any other places you can think of. The further away people are from the country, the more likely they are to buy, and at a proper price. Arrange to meet your customers at their work so they can all collect their meat at the same time and you can sell as much as possible. Farmers' Markets are not an option for the small producer unless he or she has a continuous supply of lambs, which might mean keeping several breeds of sheep. If you have any ewes that don't make the grade, run them on until early Autumn and then slaughter them with the lambs. The joints will be huge, however there is a small but growing market for mutton, a very tasty meat.

Wool

Selling your fleeces to the Wool Marketing Board is sometimes not very remunerative: with certain breeds you scarcely get paid the amount the shearer requires for his fee. Sheeps' wool is very versatile and in Germany they are more aware of this. In this country you either sell your fleeces to the Wool Marketing Board or try to find the very small niche market for spinners and weavers. However, the problem here is that these people very often produce their own wool, so unless you have some amazing fleeces, a market is hard to find. Two of the great qualities of wool are its insulation value and its reluctance to burn. There must be someone out there with some chemical and engineering skills who could come up with some good ideas and make a fortune, buying fleeces at £1 or £2 each!

Skins

If you have some attractive looking white or coloured sheep, you can buy their skins back from the abattoir for curing. There are professionals who will do this for you and it is also possible to cure them at home. The cost is about £16 to £20 per skin. See Useful Addresses at the end of the book.

Horns

If you breed horned sheep you might be interested to know that there is a market for horns. Prices will depend on the age of the animal and the breed. Stick dressing is very popular today, so it may be worth asking what sort of horns are required for this industry. Normally you are not allowed to have horns back from the abattoir as they are classified as Special Risk Material, but the stick dresser may be able to advise you on this.

Meat and Abattoirs

One of the most important reasons for keeping your own sheep is that you are growing your own meat and you know what your animals have been eating.

What weight should lambs be to go to the abattoir? The answer depends on the breed but normally they should be about 70 to 80 pounds, (30 to 35 kilos) live weight from which you get a carcass that weighs a little less than 50% of this.

The number of abattoirs in this country has been greatly reduced in recent years. This is as a result of rigorous and onerous regulations, not found in Europe, that have been imposed on British abattoirs by the Health and Safety Executive under the guise of Common Market Rulings. There are still some small abattoirs up and down the country, and they are the best to use, as when you book your animals in, you are normally given a date and a time and your animals go straight through the system on the day without layerage, (i.e. the animals stand about for a day or night stressing.) Be warned that they get extremely busy prior to Christmas so you may have to book your lambs in 2 or 3 months ahead.

The afternoon before they are due to go, bring in your selected lambs and get them ready: your local abattoir may have specific requirements such as shorn bellies for instance. Check that all ear tags are in place then pen them on straw with some water in an area where they can be loaded easily the next morning. Sometimes you are asked to arrive early at the abattoir, perhaps 6.30 a.m. so always allow plenty of time for your journey.

Fill in all your paperwork the night before you are due to go. The forms are changing all the time so you will have to contact DEFRA and the Trading Standards Office to get up to date information on what is required.

Load your lambs up carefully in the morning and allow enough time to deal with any problems that might occur. If any lambs are lame they should not be loaded. Once the animals are in the trailer push them up together with the dividing gate so that they won't be thrown about and bruised or damaged when the vehicle brakes or goes round corners. Give them plenty of ventilation.

Arrive at the abattoir on time and report to the office. They will normally unload you straight away. It is important to be punctual as everyone is allotted an arrival time slot. Once the paperwork is sorted out the lambs are unloaded and put into a holding pen before going through to slaughter.

You will normally be asked how you want your lambs cut up. Some people do their own butchery but most have their lambs jointed. You may also be asked if you want your leg or shoulder joints whole or halved, a useful option sometimes if you only want a small roast. Try to find out if your abattoir can hang your meat for you prior to butchering it. This can really enhance the flavour and tenderness of the lamb, so if it can be hung for 5 days or so, you can arrange to collect it in about a week's time.

Some abattoirs will pack and label your joints for you while others will just give you big bags full of parts, each one containing a whole lamb, which you take home and bag up yourself. Find out what the procedure is and be prepared if necessary, with large, medium and small freezer bags and labels.

The offal, (liver, lungs and heart) is available if you want it but you don't have to have it.

If you want the fleece or horns from a particular animal you will have to say so, and you will probably have to pay extra as well.

Sometimes you are asked to wash out your trailer at the abattoir but you can normally do it when you get back home. Use an approved disinfectant and don't forget to give the wheels and wheel arches of your vehicle a good squirt as well.

If you end up at home with a load of bags of lamb parts to deal with, it is certainly worth asking a friend or two to help pack, weigh and label as it is a long job, and when you have 10 or more lambs to deal with, it seems to go on for ever!

Labelling can be very simple, but it depends on what you are going to do with your meat. If it is just for family consumption then the contents and the date is enough. If you are selling it then that is another matter and you will have to take advice on it.

Chapter 7   Moving

Trailers

If you haven't got a trailer, either borrow or hire one, or better still buy one. They are always useful to have around, not only for moving sheep.

All sheep trailers have to have metal floors. Use a power washer to clean and disinfect your trailer inside and out. Power washers have come down in price, and again, come in useful for many other jobs such as cleaning cars and terraces. When the trailer is dry put in some straw to help soak up the urine and faeces during the journey, because when animals are moved they become stressed and the first thing they do is pee. Don't use shavings for the run to the abattoir as these can stick to the animals' underbellies.

There are a couple of points that should be considered when buying a trailer. If you have only a small flock, buy a low, two wheel trailer. First, if it is low, there is less drag or wind resistance than there is with a tall trailer. This could add half the price of a lamb in fuel costs if you are going to a far off sheep sale. Secondly two wheel trailers are much easier to manoeuvre by hand than four wheel or tandem wheel trailers. This is important if your reversing skills are not very good.

If you have several fields which are not connected and you have to transport your sheep from one to another, have some metal hooks or brackets bolted to the outside of your trailer to hang metal hurdles on. You will need these to make a corral for loading the sheep into the trailer.

As trailers are subject to theft, do take the precaution of immoblising them. In some parts of the country where thieving trailers is common, it is advisable to paint your postcode in large letters on the roof of the trailer. Patrols by police helicopters are alerted by a 'foreign' postcode.

Moving Sheep

Sheep are a little like computers, once they have been shown a way into a field or along a lane, they are 'programmed' to follow that route and are quite happy; but presented with a new situation like a set of hurdles or a different gateway they will be very reluctant to move.

This is where bucket training your sheep comes in useful. Do this by calling your flock while rattling a bucket half full of sheep nuts. The two sounds will come to mean something exciting to your animals, like food or fresh pasture. But you must have them in a bunch so that they can go through the gate or across the lane all in a body together. Ideally there should be two people, one leading the way and one herding the stragglers at the back and closing the gate. Young well grown lambs can be a problem as they move very fast and aren't familiar with the bucket procedure.

Chasing round after sheep not only wears you out, it doesn't do your sheep any good either. Always try to move them in the cool of the evening or on a dull day. Avoid hot weather if you can.

If you haven't the use of a sheep dog, then a quad bike is almost as good. Once sheep realise that they can't run away from a quad bike, they learn to respect it, and as soon as they hear it they know it means feeding or herding time. I did once have a ewe which could not be moved without breaking away from the others. I sold her on. It is advisable to get rid of any 'jumpers' too.

The word 'hefted' or 'heifed', (in North country parlance) only applies to hill sheep who have been living for generations in one area. They know instinctively where the best grazing is or where to shelter from bad weather. They only come off the hill for shearing or when the lambs are sent away to market, and are usually sold with the land.

Handling

When you handle your sheep you will need some wooden or metal hurdles. The metal ones are best as they interlock with each other and can form a solid barrier. If possible, try to organize a dedicated handling area in a dry place under a shady tree and accessed by a gate. If this isn't possible, a temporary one can be made. Sheep understand going through gateways as this normally means fresh pasture. They will prefer to rush through the gate into the temporary handling system, rather than being herded into a corner of a field. You are aiming to push all the sheep through in one group, so stand by the gate rattling the food bucket until they are all round you, and then open the gate and let them in. Make sure that you complete what you have to do to them, foot trimming or injections perhaps, as they will be reluctant to be caught a second time in the same way if turned back into the original paddock.

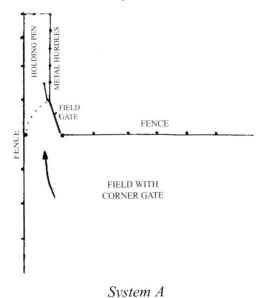

System A

This system of gathering sheep works well. Make a long holding pen with the gate at one end. Make it as long as possible so the sheep don't have a chance to turn back, and close it with a metal hurdle. Once the sheep are in they can be bunched up together. The hurdles at the end must be tied strongly to the fence and to each other, as the throng of sheep could push them apart if they are not properly secured.

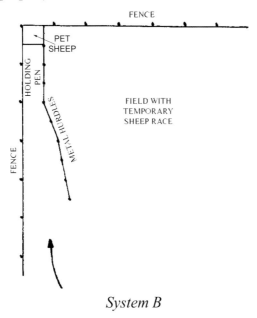

System B

This system does not work quite as well as plan A. The sheep don't know what is happening so are reluctant to enter the enclosure. If you have a pet sheep put her in the end of the enclosure as a decoy. This normally works well, and as the sheep come in you will be able to close the funnel behind them. You may need several people to help channel them in the right direction, and don't forget to tie up the hurdles securely at the end.

Once the sheep are in the handling area, push them all up together with hurdles so they have no room to jump out and are easier to catch. If there are any small lambs, pull them out and treat them first. As you take animals out of the enclosure, keep the remaining ones tightly penned up with the hurdles.

There are all sorts of handling systems available, but most are designed for the larger sheep farmer. A squeeze pen of two or three metal hurdles inside a larger holding pen should be sufficient for the small flock owner.

If your sheep appear to be having persistent foot problems, it may be necessary to make up a race with a foot bath of Zinc Sulphate. Trim the feet of the first three sheep then push them through to the bath. Once you have dealt with the forth set of feet the first animal will be ready to come out leaving room for the forth one to go in, and so on. The bath should be 3 metres long by 0.3 metres wide and will be able to take about 3 animals. Leave them to stand in the solution for about 15 minutes before letting them out. You will need a concrete area at the end of the foot bath where the sheep can stand and allow the Zinc Sulphate to dry. See also section on Footrot (page 79).

How to Hold a Sheep

Put one hand under the chin holding the jaw bone, and the other along the back with your fingers either side of the tail. Sheep move backwards best. To inspect a sheep, manoeuvre it against a wall, a fixed hurdle or a fence and push your knee into its side. This will free your hand on its back so you can look for signs of Fly Strike, or a tag number, etc.

The next step is to learn how to roll the sheep over onto its bottom. Hold the sheep against you with your right hand under its jaw grasping the wool on its neck, and your left hand reaching over its back and holding the fleece low down on its flank. Pull the sheep's head up with your right hand, and pull the body up and round with your left hand. At the same time, push with you knee into the sheep's side until the animal is sitting on the ground between your feet facing away from you, with your right hand still holding the wool under its neck. In this position you can easily lean over to examine and treat the feet, although it's very hard on your back if you have many animals to deal with.

To roll a sheep onto its back, start by manoeuvring it against a fence or fixed hurdle. Bend down, reach under the sheep and grab the two legs nearest to the fence, pull slowly and the sheep's body will slide down the fence until it is lying on its back on the ground.

There are several systems available for rolling sheep over onto their backs or sides without getting backache. There is a simple 'deckchair' system where the sheep is buckled into a metal frame with a canvas backing, and a rope or strap is placed across its chest to contain it. Then there are various makes of roll-over cages which can be expensive, but they do bring the sheep up to waist height.

Crooks

Crooks are used much less now than they used to be. There are three main types: one for catching by the leg, one for catching by the neck and the third for tripping friends up at the market!!

A crook was used when a shepherd's dog had cornered a sheep and the shepherd could then grasp the sheep by the neck with the crook. Leg crooks were mainly for catching lambs with, a useful tool for the small flock owner. It's also nice to own a well carved horn crook or market stick, especially if the horn came from one of your own animals.

Chapter 8   Lambing

Before you experience your own lambing it is important that you attend a course on lambing if you possibly can. You may not always be able to rely on your farming friend for help when you need him.

This is always an exciting time, but before it comes round, do check that you have everything ready and to hand. (See list page 54)

One word of warning: if you have a wife, friend or visitor who is pregnant, do not involve them in the operational side of lambing or feeding etc. as some sheep diseases can cause abortion, so overalls, gloves, boots and mucky hands should be treated with great care.

Lambing can take place inside or outside or a little bit of both.

Lambing Inside

(Refer to Housing page 18) There are several advantages in lambing indoors. First you can lamb your ewes during the winter months when the weather can be cruel, giving you the opportunity to keep your sheep off your land during the wettest months. This reduces poaching and allows the ground to rest until the grass starts to come through. Also, lambing inside does provide better conditions and higher survival rates during the winter months. Added to that it is much easier for the shepherd from the point of view of monitoring the ewes, feeding, handling, tagging and recording etc. The disadvantages are expense - the cost of housing, hurdles, feeders, buckets etc., the increased risk of diseases such as pneumonia due to large concentrations of animals, which would involve more use of drugs and finally, ewes bullying each other.

Lambing Outside

This normally takes place in March, April or May, depending where you live. It is a more natural system for the ewe as she can choose where to have her lambs, and another big advantage is that you don't have the expense involved with lambing indoors. Also, the risk of disease is much smaller and thus there is less need for drugs. The disadvantages are that you can only lamb in the warmer months and the lambs' survival can be affected by the weather and / or predators. Also, conditions are harder for the shepherd when he is checking up on which ewes have had which lambs and where, and when he has to catch lambs for tagging and recording. This is not such a problem for the small flock owner compared with a shepherd who has to deal with scores of animals. Lambing outside should take place on clean pasture that has had no sheep on it for at least 3 months. An old orchard would be ideal, preferably surrounded with good hedges or walls for shelter and not too far from the house. The ram has been taken away 2 or 3 months before, and the ewes are being fed daily with hay and sheep nuts. As a very rough guide ten ewes need about 10 kilos, (22lbs) of nuts per day, normally half first thing in the morning, half in the evening and as much good hay as they want. They will find a certain amount of grass too, and they must have their salt lick, their Tubbies (special mineral supplements in tubs, see Licks and Tubbies) and some water.

During the later stages of pregnancy the ewes do a lot of sitting around as they are very heavy, and you will see, when they are feeding at the troughs, that their udders have started to swell. Certain large breeds of sheep such as the Grey Faced Dartmoor, can have a tendency to get cast, that is get stuck on their backs, and the danger of this is even greater when they are heavy with lambs.

Lambing

You will notice when lambing is imminent, as a ewe will go off her food and start looking for somewhere quiet to give birth, often under a hedge or wall out of the wind. She will appear to be uncomfortable, getting up, lying down, pawing the ground with a front leg as if to make a nest, stretching her head backwards and lifting her top lip. These are all classic signs.

At the onset of birth the water bag will appear and hang out under the tail, then there may be an interval of a few hours before the lamb starts to come. When that happens you should be able to see two little feet and a nose coming into view. With older ewes the actual birth is usually very quick, perhaps a matter of minutes, but with ewe lambs (first time mothers), it can take longer. The lamb is encased in a yellowish placenta which the ewe quickly licks off while her offspring is struggling to its feet. This licking is part of the bonding process and also stimulates the circulation.

I find that the less you interfere, the better the lambing goes. You could keep an eye on the proceedings from a distance with a pair of binoculars. Some sheep do get upset with humans around, and it's very important to keep dogs out of the area as well, as they will certainly agitate the ewes, and will also be attracted to the afterbirth.

Once the lamb is up and trying to feed all should be well. One possible problem to be aware of however, is that the ewe's teat seals may not have broken. These are waxy plugs that stop infection getting inside the teat prior to lambing, and sometimes the ewe needs a little help to get rid of them. Gently squeeze the teat and when the milky colostrum starts to flow, push the lamb on to suckle. With some particularly woolly sheep it is a good idea to hand shear the area round the udder as young lambs may otherwise have difficulty finding the teats. If you are lambing in the same paddock every year or the ewe has had an assisted lambing, then you should dip the lamb's navel in iodine or spray it with antiseptic.

If the ewe has another lamb or lambs to come, there could be another interval of 1 or 2 more hours, and by the time the last lamb is born, the first should be up and suckling well.

A word about the afterbirth. Most sheep lamb at night so by the time you arrive in the morning, the afterbirth may have gone. Some sheep eat their own afterbirths, an instinct left over from their wild origins, prompting them

Foot before trimming

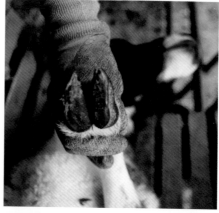

Foot after trimming

Foot trimming gear

Belly and tail shearing for abattoir

Ear tagging

Not long to wait

First signs of labour - pawing the ground

Water bag appearing

Stretching the neck backwards

Waiting to lamb

First sign of head and feet

Lamb ready to slip out

Lamb halfway out

Last stages of lambing

Breech presentation

First lamb suckling
second on the way

Second lamb suckling

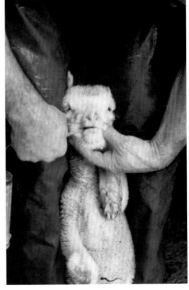

Two healthy lambs

Tube feeding

Castration

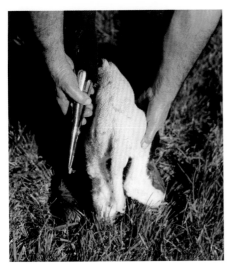 

Tail docking

Shearing

Jacob ram with a Tubby

to dispose of any trace of a recent birth and newly arrived young. It is also said that there are nutritional benefits from this. If the sheep doesn't eat it foxes and crows will, but if you can clear it up, do so and then burn it. Just be aware that some ewes don't cleanse immediately, that is, the afterbirth does not come away but trails out of the back end for a couple of days. Don't try to pull it out, it will all happen naturally.

Obviously there are sometimes problems at birth, but these are looked at later in the chapter.

The day after the birth the lamb(s) should be looking good and moving about freely. It is at this point or within the next 5 days that you should ring the tails and testicles, (see Tail Docking and Castration beginning page 56) but only when the weather is dry and sunny. Under a new ruling all lambs should also now be ear tagged with a UK number at birth, so it is probably better to wait a couple of days and tag and ring them at the same time. After a day or two you may have a job to catch them, (a crook comes in useful here) so it is best to run them with the ewes into a temporary pen on the edge of the field and catch them there. While you are tagging and ringing, note the sexes of the lambs and the ewes' ear tag numbers for your records. You can also mark the ewes and their lambs with the same number so that they can be sorted out easily if they get separated.

It's important to keep feeding the ewes until the new grass comes through. You will soon notice when they start to leave the nuts and hay, preferring the grass. At this stage remove both but leave the lick and Tubbies.

If the weather is wet and cold when the lambs are born it is advisable to bring them in for a day or two, so that they can dry out, warm up and establish a bond with their mothers. Once the weather has cleared up, put them back outside with the other ewes.

When you take the lambs into the sheltered area, pick them up and walk backwards out of the field, holding them out low in front of you so that the ewe can see, hear and sniff them. Some ewes will hug your legs and not leave her lambs for a moment, others are not quite so easy to manage! You just need patience. You may have to put the lamb down and walk a little way from it. If it is not bleating, make a lamb noise, and when the ewe comes over and sniffs it, pick it up again and continue to walk slowly backwards, holding it out towards her until you get to the sheltered area. Allow her to follow you and the lamb inside, and then close the hurdle behind them. Some young, inexperienced ewes will keep trying to go back to the place where they gave birth, or join the other ewes. They are often poor at the bonding process to begin with. In fact any problems that do arise with lambing or bonding are more likely to occur with ewe lambs having their first offspring. As they get older they should settle down and become good mums.

Lambing Procedure and Problems

If you are a beginner, it is important to read these details, and advise your sheep friend of what is going on and ask him to show you what to do.

Quite a few of the malpresentations that can occur at birth, require you to put a hand inside the ewe and feel around for lamb parts. Make sure you always have clean hands, that your nails are short and that you have no jewelry on. Women are often better at this than men, having smaller hands and arms. This is particularly important in the case of young ewes having their first lambs where the cervix is smaller. In this case you must work with the ewe, timing your movements to correspond with her contractions; it will feel as if there is a tight band squeezing and contracting round your arm.

Correct Presentation

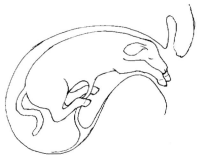

The correct way for a lamb to be born is head first with its head laid between its outstretched forelegs. Its feet have cartilage pads on them to prevent them ripping the ewe's uterus. These pads fall off after the lamb is born. If there is a problem, the head or the legs can get forced out of position; one or both legs may be bent backwards, and the lamb appears with only the head or one leg showing. In general, malpresentations are much easier to correct if the lamb is first pushed back into the uterus. This is best achieved by pushing steadily on the lamb for a few seconds. Do not use excessive force.

One Leg Back

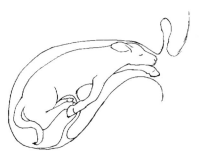

Push the lamb back into the uterus and start again from scratch. Find the two front legs and attach a rope to them, (this must be boiled or sterilized). This will make it easier to get a grip as the legs will be very slippery. Pull them and the head out of the ewe then gently ease the lamb down to the ground in line with the ewe's backbone. Alternatively, take the leg in one hand and pull gently; with the other hand ease the head out of the ewe and pull the lamb down to the ground in line with the ewe's backbone.

Both Legs Back Sometimes called 'Hung Lamb'

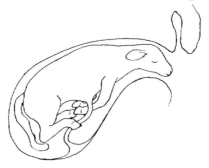

This is a little more complicated but as with the previous case, it is much easier to deal with if the lamb is first gently pushed back into the uterus then the procedure followed as before.

Hind Legs First

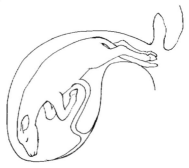

Speed is essential here since the lamb is usually pressing on its own cord which carries oxygenated blood to it until it can breathe independently. Grasp the lamb's ankles and legs; you may need to tie a cord or rope (this must be boiled or sterilized) round them to get a better purchase. Then pull out the lamb as quickly as possible, in line with the ewe's backbone or horizontally if she is standing up. This is to stop the lamb's belly from being crushed during delivery; its ribs can often get broken as well. If the ewe has twins, they will usually both be born this way.

Tail First

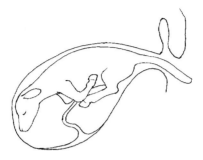

Obviously the first thing you see here is the lamb's tail hanging out. Again, speed is essential. Push the tail back into the ewe then draw out both hind legs, making sure they belong to the same lamb: if you are not careful you could find yourself holding one of the lamb's hind legs and another leg from a different, (twin) lamb, in which case no amount of pulling would do any good. Quickly draw the lamb out by the legs in line with the ewe's backbone.

In both these breech presentations there is a concern that the umbilical cord will break and / or the lamb will start to breathe in the womb, taking in womb fluid. When it is out, grab it by the hind legs and swing it rapidly backwards and forwards to get the fluid out of its lungs and windpipe. Clean any fluid or mucus away from its mouth with a towel or kitchen paper then rub the rib cage vigorously with a rough towel. If the lamb is still not breathing, try mouth to mouth resuscitation, moving the front legs backwards and forwards to stimulate the lungs into action. There are even smelling salts on the market (Dopram-V) designed to get lambs to breathe! This is all very drastic stuff, and you do need to have an experienced person with you to help out.

Two Feet Out and No Head

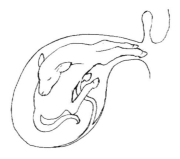

Check the feet first and note which side the points of the hooves are. They should be on top facing upwards, meaning they are front hooves not back ones. You will need a very clean hand and forearm and a long surgical glove for this job, plus some lubricating gel. Don't try to pull the lamb out as this will make matters worse, forcing the head further back into the womb. Attach a clean, disinfected cord round the lamb's two ankles and push the feet and cord back into the womb, following in with your hand. Push the legs down into the womb then feel back up the legs to the shoulder, neck and head. Everything is very warm and slippery. Now grasp the head by putting your hand on top with two fingers behind, and the thumb and fourth finger in the eye sockets. Draw the head out of the ewe and bring up the legs with the cord. Deliver the lamb by pulling it down towards the ground if the ewe is standing up.

Twin Lambs Badly Presented

Here you may have any combination of hooves and heads presented. The basic idea is to push one, or part of one lamb back into the womb and deliver each lamb in the correct way. Feeling inside a ewe who has twins or triplets is quite difficult, trying to work out which part belongs to which lamb and its position in the womb. Aim for a lamb's head and gently ease it out, bringing up the legs at the same time, then pull the lamb out down to the ground. After that lamb has recovered and is breathing, go in with a clean hand or new glove and lubricant, and gently fish around again. Make sure that it is the last lamb and deliver it as above.

I can't stress enough that most of these difficult births should be handled by an experienced person or large livestock vet. Going into a ewe's womb is a very invasive procedure, and although you may save the lamb(s), you could possibly kill the mother if she is not given the proper treatment afterwards. This normally comes in the form of an antibiotic pessary which is inserted into the womb, plus a long lasting jab of penicillin or antibiotic.

On the human side, if you have not been wearing surgical gloves, you will need a very good scrub down afterwards to stop possible infections to yourself and others, and also to your animals. You must use a proper disinfectant.

During lambing, it is important to record any ewe which is having problems and the events at the time. These notes are invaluable for future reference.

What causes malpresentation? There can be a number of reasons and it is often difficult to give a definite answer. It may be that the ewe has been chased by dogs or has been struggling in muddy conditions, but this is unlikely to be the cause. Poor nutrition during pregnancy can be a factor, and sometimes the flock can be predisposed to this condition due to seasonal variations. Whatever the reason, the ewe(s) should be recorded and given another chance.

Lamb Necessities

The most important one is your 'sheep friend' who can come over to your place with help and advice.

These are the things that are useful to have in stock, and apart from the colostrum powder, marker and iodine, the other products will keep for years.

1) A rechargeable long beam torch. This is good for flashing round the field looking for lone ewes at night.

2) A head torch. This is vital so that you can work on your sheep at night using both your hands.

3) Feeding bottles and teats. The bottles are normally plastic with measurements on. You need a couple of these and 6 to 8 teats.

4) A stomach tube and large plastic syringe.

5) A spray marker to quickly identify any problem animals.

6) Concentrated iodine for dipping navels.

7) A rope halter to tie up a ewe with if she is pushing a lamb away. This sometimes happens if the bonding is not very strong, but if she is tied up the lamb will have a chance to suckle.

8) Colostrum powder. This is quite expensive but it's worth having a small quantity in stock just in case of emergencies.

9) A bottle of 20% calcium borogluconate plus magnesium and phosphorous.

Your sheep friend will probably have any other lambing aids which at a later date you may wish to add to your medicine cupboard.

Weaning, Creep Feeding & Grazing

This is a system of weaning and fattening your lambs. It can be practiced by small flock owners, but is not essential as their lambing usually takes place later in the year. The young male lambs are normally taken from their mothers at about $4\frac{1}{2}$ months old if they are entire. If you have any pairs of male and female twins you should keep a close eye on their mothers at this stage as they will now only be suckling one lamb from one side, and this can easily lead to mastitis. I would always wean both lambs and not take the risk; this also gives the ewe longer to recover and get into condition for tupping. If the males have been castrated however, they can benefit from another 3 or 4 months with their mothers until they and the young females are taken away prior to the ram going in with the ewes. Weaning involves some fine tuning regarding timing, as the longer you can leave the young with their mother the better because this allows her milk to dry up naturally. Weaning too soon can give rise to mastitis in the ewes as they are still making milk, and it is also stressful for the lambs, resulting in runny faeces, worms, loss of condition and a lot of bleating! So if you can coincide the date of weaning with the date for the abattoir, so much the better.

The creep feeding system works as follows. A special gate or hurdle is constructed to allow the lambs forward access to graze in a field without the ewes being able to get through as well. The lambs can also enjoy supplementary feeding in weather proof troughs. The special gate has vertical round revolving bars, and the spaces between can be adjusted to the size of the lambs as they grow. This gives the lambs a measure of independence while also allowing them access to their mothers. The bond between them gradually weakens as the ewes' milk dries up. In the early lambing commercial systems, which are nearly always indoors, creep feeding is encouraged from two weeks after birth. The lambs are fed on special small pellet food, often medicated because of the concentration of animals. The food is gradually changed to a coarse mix which is designed to encourage the uptake of grass when it comes through. This latter system is designed to catch the early lamb market with the better prices, but I do wonder if the quality and flavour of the meat suffers.

Tail Docking

Most commercial owners dock their sheeps' tails. This is done with a small tough rubber ring which is stretched with a special tool called elastrator pliers. The ring is placed round the tail, about 3 fingers down from the base, and released. This stops the flow of blood into the end portion of the tail, which dies, withers and falls off after 2 or 3 weeks. It is a fairly painful operation and is done at the same time as castration. It is important to carry out these operations either when the lambs are indoors or when the weather is warm, as you may lose a lamb on frosty or wet days. Most lambs drop on the floor with the pain which lasts about an hour. Ringing and castration have to be done within 5 days of the lamb being born: it is illegal to do it after 5 days.

Is docking necessary? The answer is no although in some cases a short tail is called for by a particular breed. One only has to look at some of the French breeds to see what is meant by short, but by not docking the tails, your sheep are more vulnerable to fly strike. With hill sheep the tails are left untouched for two reasons: first, because the ewes lamb out on the hills it is impossible to get to all the lambs, let alone catch and ring them, and second, a long tail offers some protection to a lactating ewe's udder.

If you choose not to ring tails or castrate males, you do have the opportunity to select any good ram lambs for breeding. But good management is essential to ensure that your sheep don't get dirty backsides which will attract fly strike, and equally important, the ram lambs must be taken away from their mothers and any other females at four ½ months old.

Castration

If you have not done this before get an experienced person to show you how, as you could end up killing the lamb.

Load the elastrator with a ring, pick up a lamb, and using a stool, sit down holding the lamb with its back legs against its chest so that the scrotum hangs down between its legs. (Try not touch the scrotum as this might cause the testicles to retract into the body cavity.) Stretch the rubber ring and place it over the scrotum with the points of the pliers facing towards the lamb's body, then release the ring and remove the pliers. Make sure that you have two testicles in the scrotum and that the small teats either side are outside the ringed part of the body. If you make a mistake, push a small piece of wood between the ring and the skin and cut the ring with a sharp knife or razor blade. Try the operation again an hour or so later or the next day and hope that the lamb might have forgotten about the experience! If you only ring one testicle the ram then becomes a 'rig' and is a real nuisance with the ewes later on.

The main reason for castration is to allow the ram lambs to stay longer with their mothers without the risk of mating with them. Also, castrated ram lambs mature more quickly than those that are left entire. This is because the castrated animals are not using up energy developing their reproductive organs and running round thinking about sex. You will find in a mixed flock of entire males and female lambs, that the ewe lambs develop and mature faster than the boys.

Orphan Lambs

These can be a mixed blessing. You obviously want to save a lamb from certain death if the mother ewe has too many other lambs perhaps, or her milk has dried up, or worse still, she has died after lambing. Most people try to avoid the extra work involved by fostering them onto other ewes, as they are very time consuming, although if you have children about, they usually love feeding lambs.

It is sometimes advisable not to keep orphan lambs for breeding. Because of their poor start in life they often do not have a strong immune system to cope well as adults. Also, the ram lambs who have been tame and docile all their short lives, can change for the worse during the breeding season, sometimes with nasty results! Having said that, let's get on and save the lamb.

It is probably wet, cold and very weak by the time you get to it. Check its temperature by putting a thermometer up its bottom into its rectum. If the temperature is under 35°C the lamb will die soon, so act quickly. If it is around 37°C the lamb needs attention. If you have no thermometer put your little finger in the lamb's mouth; it will probably feel very cold inside. If the lamb is wet as well, rub it vigorously with an old towel, and use a hand held hair dryer to warm it. In the old days people would sometimes put chilled lambs in the cool oven of an Aga to thaw out but that is not recommended these days for health reasons.

If the lamb has not suckled or had much colostrum and is still weak, you need to give it some via a stomach tube. If you are able to gently milk some from the mother, that is obviously preferable. Otherwise mix up some powered colostrum, (50ml. per kilo of the lamb's body weight) with warm water, not too hot for obvious reasons. Draw it up using a large plastic syringe without a needle. Wet the stomach tube with warm water and gently insert it down the lamb's throat. There will be a certain amount of resistance to this, but be firm and slowly push the tube in and down until there is only 2 to 4 inches of tube left showing out of the mouth. You will know when it is in the right place, that is in the stomach and not the lungs, when the lamb starts to suck on the tube. Attach the syringe to the tube and gently squeeze in the colostrum mixture. When it is all gone, make a kink in the tube so that any milk left in the end does not flow into the lamb's lungs while it is being withdrawn. Pull out the tube gently and put the rather limp lamb in a box with some hot water bottles or under a heat lamp. A large cardboard box will do with a towel and a thick layer of newspaper underneath to soak up the lamb's pee later. The great moment comes when it lifts its head and bleats: recovery is on the way. The lamb needs 4 tube feeds in the first 24 hours. The faeces are yellow to begin with, but turn black after a few days.

The next stage is to get the lamb to suck on a rubber teat. This comes naturally to most of them, but some are slower to get the hang of it. Make a fine hole in the top of the teat with some sharp kitchen scissors; as the lamb grows bigger, so the hole can be enlarged. Teats are not expensive and we usually keep several with varying sizes of hole. The lamb will need 4 feeds of replacement ewe's milk daily and can take up to a litre or 2 pints each day, but most will not be able to manage this amount to begin with. It's great to see the tails wriggling with pleasure and the sides beginning to bulge as the milk goes down!

While you are bottle feeding your lambs, it's important to keep all your equipment hygienic, so have a bowl of hot water and Milton ready to clean your syringe and stomach tube, bottles and teats in after use.

After a couple of weeks the lambs will start to graze a bit and can be offered some lamb pellets. They should be down to half a litre or 1 pint a day each now, which they will need for another 2 weeks, and more if you let them! By this time they will be grazing and feeding along with the other lambs, but you will find that whenever you go into the field they still come rushing up to you asking for their milk bottles, rather flattering and very endearing!

Chapter 9   Records

These come in three types, two compulsory and the third useful for breeding and management information.

The first compulsory book is called a Movement Book. This records the date of movement, the addresses of where the sheep came from and where they are going, the number of sheep, male or female, and the tag numbers of these sheep, also the number of sheep on the holding. All deaths must be recorded as well. This has to be kept up to date within 36 hours of movement. Check with DEFRA for any changes to regulations.

You can keep these records in a strong exercise book with lines ruled down the page and headings, or the information can be stored on a computer. In all cases this book is a legal document, and at times of Foot and Mouth, as we have had recently, the information in it could be very useful.

The second compulsory book is the Medicine Book. Again, you can buy a strong exercise book to keep all this information in, or store it in a computer, but, like the Movement Book, it is a legal document. This book records all medicines administered to your sheep with the relevant ear tag numbers and the date, for instance, when you injected them against worms, when you drenched them or when an animal was given antibiotics.

The third book is more interesting. It is like a diary of events and records the dates of when the ram was put to the ewes, when lambing started, who had what and how, and the progress of lambs for slaughter or for breeding. It can be as detailed or as brief as you require, but is useful to look back on as a yardstick for the year to come. If you are breeding from pedigree sheep then the records need to be rather more detailed. In this case it is best to buy a proper herd book, or put all the information on a computer disk.

Marking

Marking is a temporary method of identifying animals and can be done in two ways. There are marking sticks which come in several colours and are normally applied to the sheep's head between the eyes when the animals need to be identified for some reason such as foot problems. Then there are aerosol spray markers, again in a range of colours, which are more permanent. These are what people use to write numbers on lambs' sides, rather like a form of graffiti I always think, but essential for the busy farmer when moving ewes and lambs around.

Tags

In spite of what some people say, tags are all right for short term identification purposes, but they don't last long and gradually work loose and tear out of the ear; this seems to be the experience of most farmers I have talked to, although my sheep have only lost 2 of their tags in 6 years.

The two most favoured tags are the metal and plastic clip types. There are also larger tags available which are used for milking sheep and for identifying animals at a distance. The official DEFRA tags are put onto the left ear with an applicator that looks rather like a pair of pliers. The tag is best put on the bottom of the ear towards the middle. Make sure that it is positioned well up the ear and does not hang down with space between the ear and the loop of the tag. There is normally no blood, but you can give a squirt of antiseptic spray if you wish.

The ear tags have to be specially ordered from the manufacturer and must have the following details on them: your flock number, starting with UK….. (you obtain this from DEFRA), and secondly, a number starting at 01. Tags are normally supplied in a range of colours and you can now buy them in small quantities, minimum 10. Of course you can use them for other things as well, to identify which animals are pure bred for instance.

Whether you are selling animals, taking lambs to the abattoir or moving sheep from farm to farm, you must ensure that all your stock are tagged for recording purposes. As already mentioned, DEFRA regulations state that all animals must be tagged from birth.

There are various other ways of identifying your sheep. Some breeders use an ear tattoo but I have never been able to read it very well so I do not use it on my sheep, but that's not to say it would not work for you. Other ways of recording individuals use a system of ear notching or horn colour coding on horned sheep, but the modern method that will supersede them all is electronic tagging. This can either be in the form of a transponder/chip placed under the skin or in a bolus placed in the stomach. Both systems are read by a hand held receiver that reveals the individual transponder number when passed over the sheep. On a bigger scale, they can be read by a receiver placed in a race that registers each transponder in each animal as it passes. This information can then be down loaded onto a computer at a later date, allowing the job in hand to be completed without having to read an ear tag. The receivers are quite expensive at the moment, but will probably drop in price as more are demanded. If you have joined the National Scrapie Plan, then any sheep on that scheme will have a transponder in its stomach.

Chapter 10 Breeding

Breeding

During the summer months you should look at your flock and decide which ewes you want to keep for breeding and which ones you will sell on. This decision will be influenced by what the ewes look like, how they have lambed and what their progeny is like.

It is possible to add ewe lambs to the breeding flock if they are sufficiently well grown; they normally only have single lambs the first year. With some breeds it's preferable to wait until they are shearlings about 18 months old, before putting them with the ram. You will find out details like this from the person you buy your sheep from.

Before putting your breeding flock to the ram, move them onto fresh grass and/or give them extra rations to help bring them up into breeding condition. This is called flushing.

Put down extra troughs for the ewe lambs otherwise the heavier ewes will hog their food. Do not overfeed them as fat sheep don't breed well.

Prior to flushing it is important to check your animals over. This involves looking at, and trimming their feet, checking their udders and seeing that there are two teats and no lumpy bits, and cleaning up their backsides if necessary, (dagging). Next you must look at their mouths. There should be an even row of teeth with no gaps, although it's quite common for sheep over 4 years old to lose the odd tooth. (This is called a 'broken mouth' and should not be a problem although commercial producers do not breed from sheep with broken mouths.) Certain breeds in small flocks can live up to 20 years but they will need extra rations as their grazing ability will be rather impaired. The final point to check is your animals' condition by feeling across their backs with your hand, (see Scoring page 8).

Your ram will also need a check over. Providing all the ewes had lambs last year, there is no reason to suspect that he won't do his job again in the coming season, as long as he hasn't been fighting. Check his feet and trim them if necessary, a lame ram won't work. Check his reproductive parts: the testicles should be large, equal in size and firm to the touch, and his penis should not have any abnormalities. (Here again, friendly advice can be invaluable.) Finally check his body condition, scoring. A fat ram will not breed as well as one in good shape.

The next stage is to work out when you want lambing to start. This is an individual choice based on the ewe's gestation period, (145 to 152 days, about 5 months) whether you are lambing inside or out of doors, and any seasonal, family or business commitments. A ewe comes on heat every 17 days for about 24 to 48 hours, so this why the lambing period can stretch over 2 or 3 weeks.

Lambing inside can start as early as Christmas but usually begins in January or February. Commercial producers start earlier so they can supply well grown lambs for the breeding sales in the autumn or to catch the Easter market, at a time dictated to them by the supermarkets.

Lambing outside can start at the end of February and continue until May, but it does vary according to where you are in the country. We like to lamb outside in the first or second week in April, and hope the weather is kind. Certainly the grass is beginning to grow by then.

So work backwards 5 months and you will be able to decide when to put your ram in with your ewes. It's convenient and easy to remember if you can use a date like Bonfire Night or someone's birthday.

Putting the Ram In

The ram does become very excited at this time, and there is lots of sniffing the air and the ewes' urine to find out who is on heat. He will also sidle up to them, wrinkling his upper lip. Some rams become very possessive of the ewes and will display like this as a form of aggression, particularly at feeding times, so take care and keep an eye on him at all times.

The ram is normally left in with the ewes for 3 to 4 weeks, but can be left in for up to 6 weeks. He must be taken out at this stage though, as there is the chance that he could damage the growing foetuses by knocking the ewes around, particularly at the food trough or hayrack. He will also hog the supplementary food so he is best removed to allow the ewes to settle down to a quiet gestation period.

Chart Showing Lambing Times

Rams in	Lambs out	Rams in	Lambs out
Sep-01	Jan-26	Oct-01	Feb-25
Sep-06	Jan-31	Oct-06	Mar-02
Sep-11	Feb-05	Oct-11	Mar-07
Sep-16	Feb-10	Oct-16	Mar-12
Sep-21	Feb-15	Oct-21	Mar-17

Rams in	Lambs out	Rams in	Lambs out
Nov-01	Mar-28	Dec-01	Apr-27
Nov-06	Apr-02	Dec-06	May-02
Nov-11	Apr-07	Dec-11	May-07
Nov-16	Apr-12	Dec-16	May-12
Nov-21	Apr-17	Dec-21	May-17
Nov-26	Apr-22	Dec-26	May-22

Don't forget to add 1 day in a leap year.

Chapter 11 Feeding Sheep

Sheep will graze on grass for most of the year, but after the first sharp autumn frost, the grass begins to slow down and lose its goodness. Although the sheep will continue to graze and the grass will continue to grow if the temperature is above 7degrees Centigrade, (44 degrees F) there will not be enough to sustain them and they will need supplementary feeding. This can consist of hay, ewe nuts, rolled oats or Coarse Mix.

Hay

We have written about making your own hay, but you can buy it in, from a local farmer or dealer perhaps. A small flock owner who keeps his sheep outdoors will probably only want 60 to 100 bales, depending on the weather, where he is in the country and how much grass there is about, (sheep always prefer grass to hay). A bale should cost between £1 and £2. Make sure that it is well made, as sheep are fussy about their hay. The bales should be light to handle, leafy and sweet smelling; late hay is often very stalky. Mouldy hay should always be burnt. For 10 ewes indoors you will feed a bale of hay a day, so from December until the end of March you will need about 120 bales. Remember, when sheep are eating hay they require more water than usual.

Hay must be fed in a proper hay rack otherwise the sheep will stand or lie on it and waste it. (There are several manufacturers of these, or you will find one in the book from The Gold Cockerel Series, 'The Smallholder's DIY'). Wheel the rack to a fresh spot daily, and try to keep it in the driest part of the field so that the surrounding area does not become too poached or muddy. One way to organize this is to move the rack to high ground on a Sunday for instance, and gradually move it downhill during the week, then back up again on the following Sunday but along a parallel line. Why Sunday? Well there are often more people around to help push the hay rack up hill on that day, or you may have more time to pull it up with the quad bike or tractor. Rake up any dropped hay to allow the grass underneath to regenerate.

Ewe Nuts, Rolled Oats or Coarse Mix

Coarse mix is a combination of cereals and molasses. These are all available from your local agricultural merchant. The prices vary between £3.50 to £4.50 per bag, although coarse mix is a little more expensive. They are given dry and I like to feed them first thing in the morning so the ewes have a good start to the day. I mix the nuts half and half with the rolled oats, or feed the coarse mix by itself. Carrots are also a good addition to the diet, the more variety the better. You can buy them by the bag from the same source.

For 10 ewes and one ram I use just three quarters of a two gallon bucket of food each morning. You can adjust this up or down depending on the weather; on cold frosty days or in snowy weather the sheep will require a little more, but they should finish it up in one go as any left-overs will get spoilt in the rain or will attract birds like starlings or rooks which aren't very clean. It is a good idea to have two troughs as the ram and some of the dominant ewes can be fearful bullies. Allow 3 foot, (about a metre) of trough space per animal, and move the troughs regularly after the sheep have fed.

Feeding sugar beet shreds as a supplement alongside the concentrates, (pellets, coarse mix, etc.) is beneficial to indoor breeding ewes during the 3 weeks before and 3 weeks after lambing. Take 20 kilos of shreds and put them in a bath or other suitable large container then cover them with water. Leave them to soak overnight and they will have doubled their bulk by the morning. There will be enough to feed 10 ewes for 4 days. The advantages of this food are that it provides a lot of energy being rich in sugar, and the water content is high, helping the production of colostrum, milk and foetal fluids. It is also a good source of roughage which prevents constipation, and the ewes love it!

Commercial producers use other supplementary feeds such as turnips, swedes, haylage, silage, straw and sugar beet pulp. Most of these are produced on the farm, and there is no need to buy expensive ewe nuts or coarse mix, but this option is not really open to small flock owners.

Snow and frosts are no bother to sheep, providing they can get to the hay and supplementary food in the troughs. They will need the ice broken in the water trough.

Licks and Tubbies

Licks

These are seldom mentioned but play an important part in providing the right balance of nutrition and minerals for your flock. The sheep normally enjoy licking and gnawing at them although some animals will gorge on them. There are various kinds available and you choose one to suit the soil type in your area.

Tubbies

These are plastic buckets filled with a solid mix of minerals, spices and herbs, which the animals use like a lick. Tubbies are designed to help ewes and lambs along when they most need a boost, before and after lambing and at weaning for example. There are also different ones designed to prevent various ailments. We found one which was very successful in preventing orf. We rented a field which had orf pathogens in it, and two years running our sheep contracted the disease. Then we discovered Tubbies, put the relevant one in the field, and the sheep were fine, no orf. This certainly seems to be an excellent alternative to pills or injections.

Tubbies are not expensive, about £12 to £25 a bucket, and they are a real bonus for the small flock owner. The sheep love them too!

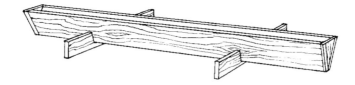

Chapter 12 Diseases and Ailments

On the whole sheep are hardy animals. Provided they are not overcrowded, have a good diet with extra rations when necessary, and have access to mineral licks and supplement 'Tubbies', they should be fine. They will also need twice yearly worming, and 'pour-on' treatment against external parasites, as well as regular foot trimming. If these guide lines are followed there should be no problems.

If you have a closed flock it means that you are not buying in ewes or ewe lambs every year, but only breed from what your ewes produce, occasionally changing the ram. Any new animals should be treated with caution. If possible try to keep them apart from your main flock for a month to six weeks to make sure that they are all right. When buying in fresh stock, try to keep to ewe lambs as they adapt better to new surroundings, and will not carry any chronic diseases.

Buying in sheep and keeping animals in large concentrations are both fairly sure ways of asking for trouble, i.e. disease. Even if you run sheep non-intensively, the land will eventually become sheep sick. Over-wintering of ewes and lambing indoors are both potential hot houses of disease, as is poorly drained land. Lowland sheep really should be used as part of a crop rotation system, being moved round regularly from field to field. For the small flock owner the secret is resting the land, topping it, rotating hay making fields, and above all, understocking it.

This may appear too simplistic, but I am all for sheep building up their own immunity. All being well, when the time comes to sell your lamb meat, you can put your hand on your heart and say honestly that the only drugs your sheep have had were wormer and pour-on treatment.

Few people mention the signs of good health in a sheep. All healthy animals have nice bright eyes of course, and as well as this, sheep in good condition love to play. (Well ours do certainly!) This consists of mock head butting and springing round the field after each other. The lambs tear around in gangs, leaping in the air, and playing 'I'm the king of the castle' on any tree stump or log. Displays like this, which often seem to happen in the late afternoon, can be very amusing and a real joy to watch.

Here is a list of some of the more usual diseases and ailments seen in sheep. It is by no means complete, and you may find that in certain parts of the country there is a prevalence of certain problems, but you should learn about anything like this from your local farmers.

External problems and diseases

Sheepscab

Thankfully this is rarely seen these days and is no longer a notifiable disease. It is caused by the psoroptic mange mite whose life cycle is 13 to 16 days meaning that it reproduces very quickly. The disease is most contagious and can be caught from neighbouring flocks. It causes the fleece to fall off leaving sore and ulcerated skin underneath. A programme of regular dipping or licensed injections will contain this disease.

Ticks, Keds, Lice and Fleas

These creatures live on the sheep and are all eradicated by the use of 'pour-on', a form of concentrated sheep dip which is squirted down the length of the sheep's spine and across the hindquarters. A ked is a wingless blood sucking beetle/lice type of creature, about a quarter of an inch long, which lives and breeds on the sheep. They have been known to bite men during shearing. In some regions and at certain times of the year, ticks and keds seem to be far more active, again, local advice on this will help.

Mastitis

This is an udder problem in lactating ewes. It is caused by the milk not being drunk from one or both sides, and an infection getting in causing the milk to thicken, clot and become blood stained. The udder will feel hot and lumpy. Mastitis is sometimes started when one of the ewe's teats becomes enlarged and too big to suckle from, so the lamb feeds from the other side all the time. The vet can provide antibiotic remedies for this, but the ewe normally loses the use of that side, or quarter. (The word 'quarter' is used for cows; these milking terms are generally shared with sheep.)

Orf

Some people get very excited about this disease because it is zoonotic, (people can catch it). You must wear rubber gloves when handling a sheep with orf. Normally it will only infect you if it comes into contact with sore or broken skin, or if you rub your face with your hand, having touched infected parts of the animal, but don't take the chance. There is no doubt that orf lies dormant in the ground and is often triggered by sheep and lambs browsing in the hedgerows and cutting their feet or mouths, allowing the infection in. The symptoms of this disease were quite often confused with those of Foot and Mouth during the epidemic of 2001. The first signs are sores, (not dissimilar to impetigo) round the animal's mouth and feet, which can spread to the udder and vulva. Spray these areas with a Terramycin spray, then put on some gloves and give the animal some Ovaloids, (Battles) capsules. These are black, bean sized pills which have to be pushed down the sheep's throat as per the instructions. If you know you have a field which harbours orf, buy yourself an anti-orf Tubby which should certainly help to cut down the risk of your stock picking up the disease.

*Pregnancy Toxaemia (Twin Lamb Disease)

This is normally seen about a month prior to lambing. It affects ewes outside that are expecting twins or triplets and are either undernourished or overweight. It is most important to provide adequate supplementary feed, and trough space for your ewes, particularly when there is snow on the ground. The symptoms include ewes standing apart from the main flock, not eating and maybe losing their sight, (this is sometimes called Snowblindness). They may twitch a little and after a few days will be unable to stand. Death follows fairly quickly. The use of a Tubby is recommended to help prevent this condition, along with balanced supplementary feeding. If you have a valuable ewe and you suspect she has this condition, you should ring your vet.

Coccidiosis

This disease occurs in lambs housed over winter or in heavily stocked paddocks. It is carried in the faeces. The lambs scour and become unthrifty. If you are creep-feeding them make sure that there is a coccidiostat in their lamb pellets or use a Tubby.

*Hypocalcaemia

This is mainly seen in the old ewe when the bones of her unborn lambs are developing inside her during the later stages of pregnancy. The demand on her calcium reserves can be so debilitating that when she lies down she can't get up again. It is obviously far better to prevent this problem than have to cure it so make sure that your ewes have a properly balanced diet, and provide them with an anti-calcium deficiency Tubby. If a ewe does develop this condition give her an injection of 100ml of 20% calcium borogluconate plus magnesium and phosphorous. Inject it slowly intravenously or into various different sites on the body to help with the take-up of the solution.

*Hypomagnesaemia

This usually affects ewes that have lambed and been put out onto grass that has been treated with nitrogen fertilizer. The lush grass has had the magnesium held back in the soil by the chemical process of the nitrogen, and as a result the ewe is deprived of this vital mineral. She will start walking stiffly and twitching, and death can follow quite rapidly so speed is essential here. Inject her with 100 ml of magnesium-fortified 20% calcium borogluconate, as with hypocalcaemia, injected into different areas of the body. The ewe will recover quickly. There are two ways you can prevent this problem from occurring: first, don't use nitrogen fertilizers but treat your field with calcified seaweed, and second, use a Tubby with a high magnesium content to ensure that your ewes get the essential minerals that they need.

* All these diseases should be treated with 20% calcium borogluconate plus magnesium and phosphorous.

Abortion

There are two main reasons for premature lambing, i.e. abortion:

1) Toxoplasma is a parasite carried by cats and foxes etc., and it will cause abortion. The oocytes or eggs of toxoplasma are eaten or drunk by the sheep, and the parasite develops inside and reaches the placenta and foetus. The result is still-born lambs between 50 to 120 days into the pregnancy. The lambs are perfectly formed and sometimes appear to be mummified.

2) Enzootic abortion is caused by chlamydia and is more often seen in ewe lambs. Abortion takes place during the last 2 to 3 weeks of pregnancy. It is caught from bought-in infected sheep, and can lie dormant in non pregnant ewes.

On the plus side, ewes do build up immunity to both these types of abortion.

Neonatal Ataxia or Swayback

This is caused by a low availability of copper in the ewes' diet which inhibits the development of the lambs' nervous system during pregnancy. Most cases occur in areas where copper deficiency is known to be a problem, or on land which has recently been improved by liming, as this procedure reduces the availability of copper to the ewe. Always make sure that your ewes are having a properly balanced diet, including the relevant Tubbies; they will get all the minerals they need from them.

Pasteurella

(remember Louis Pasteur) This is a type of pneumonia caused by overcrowding, stress, warm muggy weather and being housed indoors. This is one reason why it is so important to have good ventilation in sheep housing. The symptoms are laboured breathing, frothing at the mouth and sudden death. It kills sheep fairly quickly but normally a course of antibiotics will clear it up. It can be prevented by vaccination.

Blowfly Strike, Maggots and Clegs (Horseflies)

Sheep are vulnerable to Fly Strike anytime between May and September. Blowflies are an attractive metallic green or blue in colour. Their eggs look like clusters of white grass seed and they lay them round the rear of the sheep, round the base of the horns and feet and anywhere on the body as well. They are attracted by smell, and in the old days the shepherds in Wales would leave the wool on the sheeps' bellies so that when they were dipped, the smell of the chemical would linger on the animal. Sheep and lambs are most vulnerable on warm, still days.

Most people use a 'pour-on' treatment such as Vetrazine against blowflies, the first time a week or two after shearing and again in August. Slowly pour the correct amount of liquid down the length of the spine and across the sheep's hindquarters. This liquid can be applied with a special gun, or in the case of the small flock owner, with a large plastic syringe which should work equally well.

What to do if you get Fly Strike: It is best to check your sheep twice a day during warm spells in the summer months. Look out for an animal standing by itself under a hedge or running about in short bursts, head down, appearing to listen to the ground; or you may see an animal rubbing against fence posts or trees, and kicking or biting the wool in the affected area if it can reach, altogether very distressed. Catch it and look for maggots coming out of the wet wool where it has been biting itself. Another sign of fly strike is bare patches of skin or tufty places in the fleece where the wool is coming away. Make up a weak solution of dip in a litre plastic bottle, (Crowvect is best) then put on some rubber gloves and massage the solution into the affected areas. (If you haven't any dip a strong solution of Dettol will do.) Now watch the maggots drop out of the fleece. Cut the wool away from the area and spray any broken or raw skin with Terramycin spray. You may need to do this again after a few days to stop a further strike, so mark that animal, who will now be feeling a great deal happier with life, but may not be so easy to catch a second time round! In severe cases the sheep may need a jab of penicillin. Treat horns in the same way, pouring the solution round the head. In the case of feet, see the section on Footrot. It is very easy to miss a case of Fly Strike and not notice anything until the animal is really badly infected, so extra observation of your flock is essential during this period, particularly if the grass is lush and the sheep are a little runny behind. Blowfly strike will kill an animal if left, so act immediately.

Joint ill

This is a bacterial infection of the joints resulting in swelling and lameness. It is caused by bacteria which affect the lamb via the navel or any wound such as castration or docking. It also affects the gut if the lamb has not had sufficient colostrum.

Joint ill can be treated by a course of antibiotics. To prevent it, always ensure that your lambs get plenty of colostrum from birth to strengthen their immune systems. If a ewe dies, make up some colostrum using the powdered kind that you should have in your box of 'Lamb Necessities' (see page 54). If you are lambing indoors it is particularly important to dress the lambs' navels as soon as they are born; a high standard of hygiene is always essential indoors.

Footcare

Having a proper foot care programme is half the battle when keeping sheep, and this will be dictated by the sort of ground your sheep are running on. Sheep on heavy damp land or in straw yards, will need more attention than those on stony and drier land. In the old days shepherds would run their sheep down roads to help wear down their feet, today we have to rely on regular foot trimming.

Each foot is divided into two halves and each half has a cushiony part at the back with a layer of hornlike material round the outside. As each half grows, so the cushiony part tends to spread sideways and the horny wall grows inwards and under, thus allowing grit and small stones to become wedged in the sole of the foot. This in turn can cause the foot to become infected and can lead to foot rot.

Underside of a sheep's foot

The first sign of foot problems is lameness and sheep will often graze on their knees to relieve the discomfort. Scald in lambs is seen as lameness and stiffness in the knee joints, with the offending leg often being carried.

Dealing with sheeps' feet is very tough on your back, so if you can afford a roll-over crate, buy one. If not, use a broad wooden bench or a sheep cradle. It's also very dirty and smelly so wear old clothes or overalls, and gloves.

Trimming

Bring the sheep into the handling area and if possible run them through a foot bath to help clean their feet. You will need foot clippers, foot spray (violet), Terramycin spray and a stick marker.

Turn the sheep over onto its back in the cradle and inspect each foot. Remember, the feet are very delicate under the exterior horn and cushion, with blood vessels just beneath the surface, so go carefully with the clippers. Cut away the horny sides so that they are level with the bottom of the foot, and trim the points at the front. You will soon learn how far to go as the foot bleeds very easily. Cut back the cushion or rubbery area, particularly along the outside edge. Sheeps' feet vary in shape a lot, some are blocky and square, others long and narrow, but in a small flock you will remember the differences and trim them accordingly. When you have finished you will feel a great sense of satisfaction knowing that you have dealt with all your animals and that they should be good for the next 3 or 4 months.

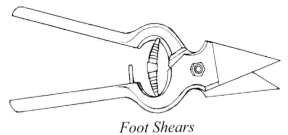

Foot Shears

If a foot is rotten you will soon smell it and it may well also be maggoty. Trim it in the usual way and cut out as much of the infected area as possible; it will be soft and whitish grey. Spray the cavity with Terramycin, and in bad cases give the sheep an injection of long-acting antibiotic in the muscle of the leg.

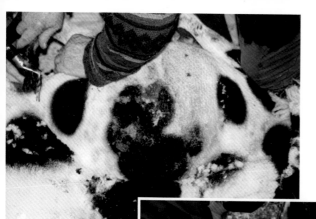

Maggot infestation revealed when shearing

'Pour-on' applied with a syringe

Swim around dipping bath

Drenching

A small sheep handling area

Indoor sheep

Foot bath

Roll-over sheep handling system

How to turn over a sheep

Young teeth

Old teeth

This will also deal with any other infected feet the animal might have. If you are not sure about tackling this job, ask an experienced sheep person to give you a hand and show you how.

Mark any sheep with foot rot on the head with a stick marker so you can keep an eye on them. They will probably be lame for a good week after the treatment, and you must be prepared to bring them in to check their feet again after a week. Put your flock onto clean grass or into a freshly strawed yard after treatment.

A zinc sulphate foot bath is an excellent way to combat foot rot. Stand your sheep in the foot bath but be careful not to use this system on hot days as they might drink the solution if they are thirsty, unless washing up detergent has been added as well; the bubbles deter them from wanting to drink. It's also very important not to allow any sheep with bleeding feet into the bath because the wetting agent used with the zinc sulphate stops blood from clotting.

If an animal is not responding to treatment after a month, keep cleaning out the foot and change the antibiotic injection. This animal should be recorded, (i.e. take a note of its ear tag number) and as soon as possible, culled from the flock. The problem might be hereditary, or the animal may have a low degree of immunity to the foot rot bacteria and thus risk spreading the infection to others in the flock.

Some people have a regular vaccination programme against foot rot which they carry out twice a year, but if the feet are regularly trimmed, there should be no need for this. It is not ideal for sheep to be injected against this and that when their own immune systems should be able to cope naturally. And besides, it's expensive!

Scald.

Strip or Sliphead are other names for this condition in lambs and old sheep: it is a bit like Athlete's Foot in humans. It can be started by long grass cutting into the two halves of the feet or impacted feaces in the feet. The infection starts up after a wet spell. High density stocking can make scald more likely as can damage to the feet from climbing up on wire fences

Bring the ewes and lambs into the handling area. Pick out each lamb and perch it with its bottom on the top of the metal hurdle. Check and gently trim each foot, cleaning out any impacted faeces which sometimes become wedged into the sole of the foot. Spray with Terramycin. You can also dip each foot up to the leg in some concentrated iodine in a jam jar. The lambs run round with ginger socks for a couple of days and the Scald usually goes away, but you sometimes have to repeat this process after a week for the worst cases. Deal with larger sheep in the same way. It seems that, as with foot rot, certain ground appears to harbour this bacteria, as it crops up regular as clockwork each year.

Internal Problems, Worms, Scrapie and Teeth.

Roundworms (not Nematodirus):

Roundworms live in the gut, the Abomasum and the intestines of the sheep, and their life cycles are basically all the same, except for Nematodirus. The male and female roundworms mate in the gut and the female will produce masses of eggs that pass out of the sheep with the dung. If the temperature and moisture conditions are favourable, the eggs will hatch and go through two larval stages, living off the bacteria in the dung, until they develop into third stage larvae. It is only at this stage that they become infective to the sheep, at the two other stages they will be digested by the animal if eaten. The third stage larva burrows into the gut wall where it stays for a week before emerging as an immature adult which will soon begin mating, so starting the whole process all over again. When winter comes, all the worms burrow into the gut wall and hibernate until spring. This build-up of egg laying worms in the gut will have little effect on a well fed adult sheep in good condition. The adult ewe's immune system will control these worms for most of the year except during the period of late pregnancy, lambing and early lactation.

During this period the ewe's immune system is suppressed and all the hibernating worms emerge at once producing billions and billions of eggs, more than they could produce in the whole of the rest of the year combined. Lambs however, are very susceptible to worms, and now there are billions of eggs going through the larval stages just waiting for the perfect conditions of midsummer to become third stage larvae that will cause serious, severe illness and even death to a lamb. Unlike the first and second stage larvae, the third stage can withstand extremes of heat and cold, with some always surviving the winter to start reinfecting again the next year. You may need to worm lambs every month for the first spring, summer and autumn.

Nematodirus

Although it is a roundworm it has a different lifecycle from the others. It is not usually a problem for adult sheep but, as with other roundworms, it can have a devastating effect on grazing lambs. These worms' eggs are passed out onto the grass in the same way as those of other roundworms, but they complete their different stages within the protection of the egg's shell. The larva is slow to develop to the third infective stage, and is very resilient to all extremes of weather. It can live in the soil for at least two years if not longer. It waits inside its egg ready to hatch when the conditions are right. This is usually when the temperature for the previous 24 hours has averaged about 10 degrees celsius after a cold spell, and can occur any time from February to June. Because conditions for the mass hatching of worms have to be fairly specific, they can be predicted and are usually widely advertised at the time. Lambs that are most at risk from a major outbreak of worms, that could cause the deaths of a third or more, are those of 6 to 8 weeks old, grazing outdoors.

Tapeworms

These are not normally a problem except in one form that can cause a nervous disease called Gid. A lamb with a heavy infestation can develop a blocked gut, but if you are treating it for Nematodirus, use a specific wormer that deals with both worms then the tapeworms will be controlled. Gid is a common problem because the dog and fox tapeworm uses the sheep as an intermediate host. (Most dogs are regularly wormed however these days.) While it is inside the sheep the tapeworm causes a cyst to grow on the sheep's brain resulting in the animal holding its head in a strange position and developing blindness in one eye. The sheep will start to go round in circles and if the cyst continues to grow, she will eventually collapse, go into a coma and die. The cyst can be removed surgically if caught in time, and the sheep can make a full recovery.

Liver Fluke

Immature liver flukes eat away at the sheep's liver, and if they are in large enough numbers they will cause major damage leading to death. The one thing on the shepherd's side is that the liver fluke needs the services of the mud snail to complete its life cycle, and if you can eliminate these creatures then you may not need to worm for liver fluke. Having said that, it is virtually impossible to get rid of them completely, unless you employ a flock of ducks perhaps! These could probably do quite a good job, although they may not be a practical proposition for everybody. The snails do not need a pond, only wet ground such as where tractor wheel ruts are holding water or in naturally boggy ground where reeds are growing, a good indicator of wet ground, or round a water trough. Use a wormer that will kill immature fluke, and move to fluke free ground, or worm every three weeks until the snails and their habitat have been destroyed.

Wormer (Also Called Anthelmintics) Groups

There are three basic sheep wormer groups (different chemicals) and they are Benzimidazoles (White Drenches), Imidazothiazoles (Levamisole) and Avermectins.

Benzimidazoles

These chemicals are generally called white drenches. They have been around since the 1960s and make up a large number of wormers. Some kill all stages of roundworms but some will not kill those hibernating worms and larvae that are important at certain times of the year. Some will also kill tapeworms and liver fluke. Some should not be used on pregnant sheep. They work by stopping the worm getting to its food supply and starving them to death. They have a good safety margin too.

Imidazothiazoles

The only chemical in this group that can be used for sheep is Levamisole which kills roundworms and lungworms but not liver fluke. It works by paralyzing the worms which are then digested, but its safety margin is not so good so avoid large overdoses.

Avermectins

There used to be only one wormer in this group but now there are quite a few, and some of the newer ones have a persistency, (they work for days or weeks after dosing.) They are effective against roundworms and lungworms at all stages including the hibernating stage, but not the eggs, tapeworm or liver fluke. They kill by paralyzing the worm and have a good safety margin but must not be used on milking flocks. The new generation of Avermectins can be bought as an injection which kills both internal and external parasites such as Sheep Scab.

When To Worm

Before you start drenching or injecting your animals you must think about the withdrawal periods of the drugs you are going to use, that is how long you have to wait before it is safe to eat the meat of these animals. So any sheep, be they destined for lamb or mutton, should not be treated if the slaughter date is within the withdrawal period.

Adult ewes will have a certain amount of immunity to roundworms, found in the gut, and will show no signs of infestation except maybe a dirty backside; so some would say there is no need to worm your adult sheep, only your young stock from 0 to 2 years old. If you selectively breed only from those adult male and female sheep that have clean backsides, and sell all those who fail this test, then in theory you will breed sheep that are immune to worm infestation. If you have an extensive grazing system with plenty of land and few animals, and can put your sheep on relatively clean pasture, then this system is possible. If you have only a small amount of land however, and more than enough sheep to utilize it, then this system will probably not work, and you could end up with more problems caused by not having wormed for years! Having said all that, I worm my ewes three times a year for roundworms, at tupping, at housing and at turning out.

Scrapie

Scrapie does not come under the heading of external parasites but has the same clinical signs as both Fly Strike and Sheep Scab as it causes the sheep to scratch or rub or sometimes bite its body. So if you have treated the animal for Fly Strike and Scab and it is still scratching, then the problem could be Scrapie. Scrapie has been around for hundreds of years and yet very little is known about it. It is a prion disease that is very slow in showing any symptoms, and it usually, but not always, affects older animals from 2 to 5 years of age. It can show up any time of the year. It is a disease which makes the animal itch and eventually die. Because the itch never goes away the animal stops eating and just spends its time scratching day and night. There is no known cure and culling the animal by humane slaughter is the only option. There is a National Scrapie Plan being put into operation which is starting by blood sampling all rams to test for resistance to Scrapie. This is called genotyping, which it is assumed will be carried forward to include all ewes eventually. This means that only animals with a high resistance to Scrapie will be allowed to mate, as those with a low resistance will be culled. The scheme is still in its infancy, and at the time of writing, my own flock is due to be blood sampled in June 2002. The big fear is that Scrapie in sheep is the same as BSE in cattle, but at the moment nobody knows one way or the other.

Teeth

Sheep are nibblers and fussy eaters. Unlike cattle which will eat whatever is put in front of them, sheep will pick the best grasses out of the pasture or the fodder and leave the rest, sometimes even to the point of starvation. They have a set of eight incisor teeth on the lower jaw called broad teeth and none on the top at the front. Further back in the mouth they have a set of molars on both sides of the jaw, top and bottom. The upper jaw just has a hard plate at the front with which they trap the grass between it and the lower jaw teeth. There is a gap between the front incisors and the molars at the back which are the teeth the sheep uses when it is chewing the cud.

When a lamb is born it has eight milk teeth on the front of the lower jaw and a full set of molars at the back. With a bit of experience you can work out a sheep's approximate age, because at one year old the first two true incisor teeth, (broad teeth) push out the middle two milk teeth. (Two Tooth) This continues each year, with the two next outside milk teeth being replaced by broad teeth, until at four years old the sheep has a full set of eight broad teeth, (incisors) on the front lower jaw. This is called a full mouthed sheep, and the teeth will stay like this until it loses some or all of these front ones naturally with age. It then becomes what is called broken mouthed. Broken mouthed sheep will usually be the ones that are looking thin and are finding it more difficult to consume enough grass to stay in good condition. This is because with fewer teeth to nibble the grass, it takes more nibbles to make a mouthful and therefore longer to graze than with a full mouth. This is the time when most shepherds will remove these sheep from the flock, and replace them with young stock which all have good teeth. The cost of feeding broken mouthed sheep from a bag is prohibitive not to mention time consuming.

Predation

This takes the form of crows, (Hooded and Carrion) foxes, badgers and dogs.

Crows

They will not kill your sheep or lambs but are attracted by the afterbirth. They also have a nasty habit of pecking the eyes out of a weak lamb or a ewe on its back (cast). This is more common in the remoter parts of the country but you should be aware of it.

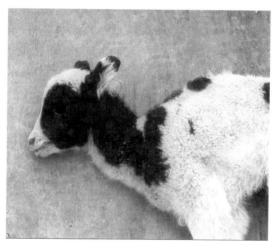

A lamb with its eye pecked out

Foxes

They will take lambs and anyone who tells you differently just does not know. Lambing often comes at a time when vixens are feeding their young. They are attracted by the afterbirth and this leads to them taking weak or unattended young as well. (The mother ewe may be giving birth to another lamb at the time). I have seen foxes in daytime quartering a field looking for lambs. They have also been known to kill ewes caught in brambles, stuck in fences or cast on the ground. They are not normally a problem as long as their numbers are controlled.

Badgers

Badgers are protected by Law. They are not usually any trouble except for the occasional rogue badger, that is one that is old or wounded and lives on its own like a tramp because it has been pushed out of the set. If one of these gets a taste for lamb, you could have a problem on your hands.

Dogs

They are not exactly predators, but when 2 or 3 dogs get together, 'hound mania' can easily set in and they will kill just for the hell of it. They don't have to be in packs either; single dogs are just as capable of sheep worrying. If you think you have a problem you should always get in touch with the Police before you do anything drastic like shooting the troublemakers.

Vets

In the beginning when you are first starting with your sheep, there may well be occasions when you feel there is something wrong with one of your animals, and you don't know what to do. Most books advise you to contact your vet if you are worried, but more often than not the problem will be minor or turn out not to be a problem at all. This could end up being very expensive for you and a waste of time for a busy vet, so it's vital that you have someone you can turn to for help when necessary. This is where your local sheep-owning friend can be very useful with advice about whether or not the situation is serious enough to warrant calling the vet. If you do have a sick ewe it is actually cheaper to take it to the surgery than for the vet to come out to you. Ideally, if you are looking after your flock correctly, you should only need vets for advice on health plans or sewing up prolapses and any gashes from accidents.

Dealing With A Dead Sheep

There is an old saying that sheep have only two aims in life, one is to get out and the other is to die! It is bad enough coming out in the morning and finding one of your ewes dead, and worse still if the carcass has been mauled by foxes. Sheep do have a habit of dying quite suddenly, but fortunately it doesn't happen very often.

Make a note of the ear tag number to record in the Movement Book and take a look at the sheep to see if there any clues as to why it died, then remove the body quickly as in hot weather it will become bloated and very smelly. Use a wheelbarrow to carry it off the field. Lay the wheelbarrow down beside the sheep and roll it in, at the same time righting the barrow.

As of April 2003, all dead farm animals must be sent to one of the following DEFRA approved places for disposal:

A. A knackers yard

B. A hunt kennel

C. An incineration company

D. A rendering plant

There may well be a charge for the services they provide. All other methods of disposal are illegal.

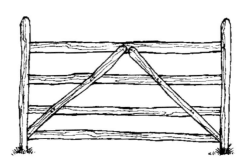

Conclusion

Having read this book you may feel that keeping sheep is not for you: your life is full of business commitments, and it would be too much like hard work. But it is interesting how sheep keeping can be woven into a busy life enriching it with new experiences, and of course you would be able to enjoy your very own produce at your own table. Sheep keeping is a way of life, and getting to know your sheep is fascinating as each animal has its own temperament, and each breed its challenge. If you do decide to go ahead, start on a small scale, build up gradually, and enjoy planning your new flock. You will soon find you develop your own routine, and things should run smoothly in no time. Above all, enjoy your sheep and take pride in them.

"There were two men in one city; the one rich, and the other poor.

The rich man had exceeding many flocks and herds;

But the poor man had nothing, save one little ewe lamb, which he had bought and nourished up; and it grew up together with him, and with his children; it did eat of his own meat, and drank of his own cup, and lay in his bosom, and was unto him as a daughter..."

The Second Book of Samuel, Chapter 12

Useful Names and Addresses

Abattoirs. Telephone your nearest branch of DEFRA.

Ascott Smallholding Supplies, Dudleston Heath, Ellesmere, Shropshire, SY12 9LJ Tel: 0845 1306285 A good range of smallholding equipment and books. Mail order.

Denis Brinicombe, Fordton Industrial Estate, Crediton, Devon, EX17 3BZ Tel: 01363 775115 Severn Farm Industrial Estate, Welshpool, Powys, SY21 7DF Tel: 01938 555906 Tubbies and nutritional supplements.

The British Wool Marketing Board, Wool House, Roydsdale Way, Euroway Trading Estate, Bradford, BD4 6SE Tel: 01274 688666 Wool sales.

Country Smallholding, Fair Oak Close, Exeter Airport Business Park, Clyst Honiton, Exeter, Devon, EX5 2UL Tel: 01392 888588 A monthly magazine for the smallholder with lots of information and advertisements.

Country Superstores Ltd. (Atlantic) The Old Mill, Earsham, Bungay, Suffolk, NR35 2TQ Tel: 01986 894745 Sheep equipment, shop and mail order.

DASH (Devon Association of Small Holders) Ted and Jenny Jury, Higher Gatehouse, Blackdog, Nr. Crediton, Devon, EX17 4RA Tel: 01884 860742 A particularly good organization with a monthly magazine advertising sheep etc. plus lists of courses and lots of other information. There are similar organizations round the country.

DEFRA (Department for Environment, Food and Rural Affairs) Look in your local phone book. Information on registration, animal movements, tagging, abattoirs, etc.

Farmers' Guardian, Olivers Place, Fulwood, Preston, Lancs. PR2 9ZA Tel: 01772 557240 A weekly newspaper for farmers, good advertisements.

National Sheep Association, The Sheep Centre, Malvern, Worcs., WR13 6PH Tel: 01684 892661 A very helpful organization for anything to do with sheep.

Peasridge SS Ltd., Stonelink, Stubbs Lane, Brede, Nr. Rye, East Sussex, TN31 6BL Tel: 01424 882900 Specialists in sheep equipment and veterinary products.

Rare Breeds Survival Trust, National Agricultural Centre, Stoneleigh Park, Warwickshire, CV8 2LG Tel: 02476 696551 For information on rare breeds of sheep, shows, and sales of rare breeds.

The Royal Agricultural Society of England, National Agricultural Centre, Stoneleigh Park, Warwickshire, CV8 2LZ Tel: 02476 696969 Organises the largest agricultural show in Great Britain, usually in the first week in July.

Skin Curing: June Tinnion. June works for a skin curing company near Bridgwater, Somerset, and handles all private orders from home. Call her before your animals go for slaughter. Tel: 01278 722570

Smallholder Magazine, 3 Falmouth Business Park, Bickland Water Road, Falmouth, Cornwall, TR11 4SZ Tel: 01326 213333 A monthly magazine for the smallholder with lots of information and advertisements.

Index

Tubbies 45, 47, 68, 69, 75
Tupping 11, 84

Udder 46, 56, 72

Vet 10, 18, 53, 73, 87
Votex mower 21

Water 17
water bag 46
wethers 6, 8
Wiltshire Horns 3, 29
Wool 6, 28, 33, 35
Wool Marketing Board 28, 29
Worm 8, 83
worm burden 16
Wormer 70, 82
Worming 13, 70
Worms 80

Zinc Sulphate 8, 42, 79